D1082978

THE STORY OF ENGLAND'S HOSPITALS

THE STORY OF
ENGLAND'S
HOSPITALS

by

COURTNEY DAINTON

with a Foreword by

LORD AMULREE, M.D., F.R.C.P.

LONDON

MUSEUM PRESS LIMITED

First published in Great Britain by Museum Press Limited
26 Old Brompton Road, London, S.W.7
1961

MADE AND PRINTED IN GREAT BRITAIN BY
HAZELL WATSON AND VINEY LTD
AYLESBURY AND SLOUGH

(R. 3371)

PREFACE

ALTHOUGH there are many books containing histories of individual hospitals, there are few describing the general history of the hospitals of this country as a whole. This is an attempt to help in remedying the deficiency. For the most part it is concerned with the social history of hospitals; only in the last fifty years have politics played a large part in the development of our hospital service. The various steps taken during this period towards the establishment of a National Health Service are briefly summarised in Chapter VIII.

The writer of such a history as this owes much to other authors. The names of those whose works I have consulted and the titles of their books are included in the bibliography. I should also like to express my thanks to Sir Zachary Cope for reading the manuscript and making some very helpful suggestions; to the staff of the Public Library at Godalming, who obtained copies of many of the books which I consulted; and to Lady Diana Cooper and Messrs. Rupert Hart-Davis for permission to quote extracts from Lady Diana's autobiography *The Rainbow Comes and Goes*.

COURTNEY DAINTON

CONTENTS

Preface   *Page* 5

Foreword by Lord Amulree, M.D., F.R.C.P.   11

I   Hospitals of the Middle Ages   17

II   St. Bartholomew's   35

III   St. Thomas's Hospital   49

IV   The Age of Hospitals   61

V   The Age of Hospitals (*continued*)   78

VI   The Age of Specialisation   93

VII   Years of Reform   113

VIII   Towards a National Health Service   129

IX   The Sick in Mind   140

X   The Sick in Mind (*continued*)   151

XI   A National Hospital Service   167

       Bibliography   176

       Index   181

7

ILLUSTRATIONS

(Between pages 96 and 97)

1. A Surgical Operation and Heating the Surgeon's Instruments, from the Early 12th-century *Astronomia medica*

2. St. John's Hospital, Oxford, erected in 1233, from a 15th-century MS.

3. Six Stages in a Brain Operation, from a medieval MS.

4. The Pest-house at Odiham, Hampshire

5. A 13th-century Hospital

6. Hospital, Middlesex, by Rowlandson and Pugin, from *The Microcosm of London*

7. Rahere Ward, St. Bartholomew's Hospital in 1832

8. A Ward in the Hampstead Smallpox Hospital, 1870

9. St. Thomas's Hospital on the Albert Embankment, in 1871

10. Princess Mary Ward, East London Hospital for Children, 1878

11. Waiting to see the Doctor at the Seamen's Hospital Dispensary, London Docks, 1881

12. A Bad Accident Case, London Hospital

13. The Bath Lift, Middlesex Hospital

14. The Operating Theatre, London Hospital, about 1900

15. The Operating Theatre, King's College Hospital, 1914

16. The Operating Theatre, Maida Vale Hospital

17. Part of the X-ray Department of the City General Hospital, Sheffield

18. The Children's Waiting-room in the Out-patients' Department of St. James's Hospital, Balham

19. Nurses' Station, Cubicle Block, West Cumberland Hospital

20. Male Geriatric Bed Ward, West Cumberland Hospital

21. Geriatric Bed Ward, West Cumberland Hospital

22. Geriatric Four-bed Ward, West Cumberland Hospital

23. The West Cumberland Hospital as it will appear when completed in 1964

ACKNOWLEDGMENTS

The author and publishers wish to record their thanks for permission to reproduce illustrations as follows: 1, the Dean and Chapter of Durham Cathedral; 2 and 3, the Trustees of the British Museum; 5-15, Radio Times Hulton Picture Library; 16, the Board of Governors of the National Hospitals for Nervous Diseases; 17, Sheffield No. 1 Hospital Management Committee; 18, the Wandsworth Group Hospital Management Committee; 19-23, Messrs. C. B. Pearson & Sons, Architects.

FOREWORD

THE recent discovery of the remains of a Roman military hospital at Inchtuthill, in Perthshire, followed by the report of a similar discovery in Wales, has put back the dating of the first known hospital in this country by several hundreds of years. It may well be that more of such hospitals remain to be discovered, and it may even be possible that buildings, hitherto unrecognised as being hospitals, will turn out to have been built for that purpose. Certainly, we have a fair knowledge of the equipment of Roman hospitals and of the various implements used in them for the treatment of patients, and we can assume that similar equipment and instruments were available in these, British, hospitals.

Of the early hospitals in this country few clinical records remain, and we do not know much of the type of patient who was admitted to their beds, or what kind of treatment was given to them. Some useful information can be found in the rolls of the Infirmerers of the great monasteries and abbeys. The Infirmerer was one of the chief officers of the monastery, and was not himself a doctor, but was appointed to his post for his administrative ability. In fact, monks were not supposed to practise medicine, and at Lacock, for example, the Infirmerer was forbidden to treat fevers, to change bed clothes, to give medicines, or to lay on plasters, except on the orders of the physician. Officials to take care of the sick were appointed—for example, at Norwich there was a "keeper of the sick" and a "servitor of those bled." The Infirmerer's rolls contain records of all purchases made and of expenses incurred on behalf of the infirmary, no matter in what capacity. The contents of these rolls, in so far as they relate to repairs or alterations of the buildings, purchase of furniture, equipment, herbs and drugs, have been published quite extensively, but most of the medical details, where they exist, have been cheerfully omitted as being of no general interest. But it may be that there do lie, untranslated and even unnoticed among these rolls, some clinical and medical details that might be of interest. References to surgery occur in the rolls, while diseases of the shin bone or tibia are not uncommon: these were treated by applications of white wine. Male nurses were sometimes employed: there is a reference to John Kyngertine who was a patient in the infirmary at Westminster in 1412 where he was cared for by a male nurse. These nurses were ordered to endure the foulness of sick persons whether in vomiting or other matters. The additional payments made to the washer-woman at Westminster because of the "debilitatem fratris Richard de Redyng" sounds suspiciously like washing the foul linen of an incontinent old man.

The Infirmerer could, and did, call in doctors from outside the monastery to visit and treat sick monks in the infirmary, and there are many records of this being done. Many monasteries entered into contracts with the local doctor to treat the monks when they were ill. It is interesting to read that the great John of Gaddesdon was called in to advise on the treatment of a sick monk in the abbey at Abingdon, for which he was paid a fee of 13s. 6d.

The monkish infirmaries had yet another purpose, and that was to supply a refuge for those elderly monks who, by reason of age and infirmity, were no longer able to carry out their duties in the monastery. Monks did live to an advanced age, their average age at death being considerably higher than that of the population outside their walls. At the abbey of Westminster, for example, the average age at death for 140 monks between the years 1261 and 1530 was sixty years. One can see here how these infirmaries might well be held to be the precursors of the old "chronic sick" wards. The infirmaries were used, too, to house monks at the time of their regular bleedings, which were carried out six or seven times a year. Monks, too, were sometimes admitted to the infirmary when they were feeling the strain of monastic life, and were suffering from "the irksomeness of the cloister, from the silence, the fasting, from the services, the overwork, from sleeplessness, from heaviness in the head and from pains in the stomach." They were not kept long in the infirmary, but were sent to a rest home in country outside the abbey. For example, there was such a hostel for the monks of Westminster in Battersea and in Wandsworth, while at Romsey there was a garden used for this purpose and for general convalescence. Here, in order that the patients should not lie in bed too long, the Infirmerer was ordered to be up early himself and see that the patients got up too. These must be among the first examples of the neurotically ill, as opposed to the physically ill, being afforded special treatment for their illness.

Food and clothing were distributed to the needy at the monastery gates, but lodging in the infirmary was confined to members of the monastery, both monks and the lay brethren. In some instances the infirmary was open to a small number of substantial benefactors or to persons who had made a regular contribution, each year, to the funds of the monastery on condition that they would be cared for within its walls when their need for such care became urgent.

We can learn from monastic records, too, much about the views and practices of one of the most enlightened of medieval societies on environmental hygiene. The records of the monastery of Christchurch, at Canterbury, for example, show how a wholesome supply of water was ensured for the monks and other residents in the buildings by methods which would find favour among many water suppliers of today. The source of the supply was an isolated and uncontaminated spring, from which water was piped through a rather primitive filter into a series of settling tanks, where it remained for some time. From these it was piped to a number of stand-pipes, of which that for the infirmary was the first, followed by others to supply the lavatorium, bath house, kitchen, etc. The water at the end of its circuit was used to flush the rere dorter, or necessarium, before going to waste. Particular attention was always paid to the siting of monasteries and their infirmaries: for a variety of reasons these were usually situated in a secluded spot, close to running water, into which the effluent from the rere dorter was discharged, downstream from the conventual buildings. These surroundings were not only conducive to the peace of mind of the inhabitants, but, even when the buildings were not so secluded, gave the monks an easy and safe way of disposing of their waste products of all sorts. The Romans, centuries before, had been able to supply the inhabitants of Rome with a wholesome water supply, brought to the city by great aqueducts, on a scale which has been estimated at forty gallons per head per day. Greek hospitals were generally situated, too, in surroundings which would induce peace and rest for both residents and visitors. While the great row of temples occupies a prominent place in the sun on the rocky crest at Agrigento, the temple of Aesculapius, which was also the centre for medical consultation and treatment, is placed in a quiet, green valley, near the sea, where a small stream still flows peacefully: an ideal spot in which to recover from illness.

Some of the medieval hospitals must, too, have been peaceful and attractive places. The great hall of the Hospice at Beaune, with its fine bed curtains and coverlets, its well-made pewter equipment and magnificent pictures, would compare well with a good hospital ward today, while in England, the little hospital of St. Mary at Chichester still retains its attractive features, but it has been turned into more of an almshouse than a hospital as we know the word. But it is surely doubtful whether a number of hospitals during the Middle Ages and later did not consist essentially of accommodation for the elderly and chronically sick, rather than for the acute sick as we know them today. These latter were often, if not usually, nursed in their own homes, where they either died or recovered—more from the lucky fact that the natural conclusion of most diseases is towards resolution rather than death, than to any skill of their doctor.

The hospital at Soutra, in Scotland, founded by King Malcolm IV in 1164, looked after not only the pilgrims (making their journey between Edinburgh and the great shrines of the border country) and the poor, but sickly people as well. It was well situated on the great road to the south, and near to it was a well whose water was reputed to have great therapeutic value. A fragment of the hospital known locally as the "Soutra aisle" is still to be seen on a bare hill in East Lothian.

Much satisfactory progress was made in surgical treatment towards the end of the Middle Ages, notably by remarkable people like Ambrose Pare, whose work revolutionised the treatment of the wounded in war. But this work was, for the most part, carried out in military hospitals, which were often of a temporary nature, and in times of war. These military hospitals, and their staff, were often protected by treaties signed by the leaders of the opposing armies in terms which foreshadowed the first Geneva convention of 1863.

Mr. Courtney Dainton has written an interesting book on the hospitals of this country, their origin, their development, their work and their future. The story he tells is one which will appeal to many who have worked in or who are interested in the growth of these great institutions. He has looked for his material widely and has chosen from it wisely. The story of our hospitals has not been told in such detail before—in fact, the subject seems to have been generally neglected; but anyone who reads this book will be fascinated by the tale, and, perhaps, amazed at the extent to which a surprisingly efficient hospital system came to work in this country many years, if not centuries, before the National Health Service was thought of.

AMULREE

CHAPTER I

HOSPITALS OF THE MIDDLE AGES

IT seems probable that the first hospitals in England were built by the Romans, although no traces of any of them have yet been found. In fact, the only Roman legionary hospital so far discovered in Britain was not unearthed until 1958. This was not in England, but in Scotland, at Inchtuthill, near Perth. It had long corridors around a central court and there were sixty wards where the sick and wounded Roman soldiers were restored to health. It is unlikely that the Romans would have constructed a hospital in Scotland and none in England, and so we may probably safely assume that they also erected the first hospital in the latter country.

The earliest hospitals of which we have any definite knowledge were the work of the Saxons. They were at St. Albans, where a hospital is mentioned in 794, at Flixton in Yorkshire and in York itself, where King Athelstan founded St. Peter's Hospital in 937. These, like other early hospitals, were not intended solely for sick people. Their purpose was indicated by their name, which was derived from the Latin adjective *hospitalis*—concerned with *hospites* or guests. These "guests" were any persons in need of shelter.

This conception of hospitals persisted throughout the Middle Ages. When a charter was granted to the hospital at Flixton in the reign of Henry VI it was stated that the building was to be used "to preserve travellers from being devoured by the wolves and other voracious forest beasts." The travellers who used them were mostly pilgrims on the way to or from one of the shrines. The Saxons were for the most part a stay-at-home people, yet some of them went on pilgrimages even to distant Rome. The Norman conquest was followed by a great increase in the number of pilgrims, and so the need for places where they could rest on their journeys became far greater. The Norman era also saw the foundation of many monasteries, and the monks regarded it as a religious duty to provide shelter for pilgrims. At first there was a *hospitium* within the abbey gate, then it was built outside the abbey walls, and gradually became an independent establishment.

The early foundations were not all known as hospitals. Many of them were intended for the support of infirm and aged people, and were called almshouses, bedehouses, Maisons Dieu or God's houses. Those intended mainly for the sick were usually called spitals or spittle houses.

The number of early hospitals of which we have record is surprising, particularly when it is remembered that at no time during the Middle Ages can the population of England have exceeded four millions. In her book *The Medieval Hospitals of England*, published in 1909, Rotha Mary Clay listed well over seven hundred establishments founded between the Norman conquest and the middle of the sixteenth century. The earliest of these was St. Wulstan's Hospital at Worcester, which was founded by Bishop Wulstan about the year 1085.

Some of these early hospitals were intended especially for lepers. One of these, at Harbledown, near Canterbury, could accommodate a hundred inmates. It was built by Archbishop Lanfranc before 1089. These leper hospitals were often known as lazar-houses, because many of them were founded and administered by the Order of St. Lazarus of Jerusalem, which was a branch of the better-known Knights of St. John of Jerusalem. The Order's chief establishment was at Burton Lazars, in Leicestershire. Because of the risk of infection the lazar-house was usually on the outskirts of the town. Normally it consisted of a group of cottages and a chapel.

Two of our most famous hospitals were founded during the twelfth century. They were both in London and we are fortunate in knowing more about their early history than we know of that of most hospitals.

St. Bartholomew's was founded about 1123 by Rahere, who is described as "a courtier though a cleric." While in Rome on a pilgrimage he was taken seriously ill and vowed that if he recovered he would build a hospital. He was restored to health and on his return to England he sought the help of the Bishop of London in carrying out his vow. The Bishop used his influence to get Henry I to provide a site at Smithfield, and there the famous hospital was founded. It was dedicated to St. Bartholomew because he had appeared in a vision to Rahere during his illness. Rahere himself assisted in the treatment of the patients, although his methods were those of a faith-healer rather than a physician. When a woman with a badly swollen tongue was brought to him, he shook his relics of the Cross, dipped them in water, wished the patient's tongue was better, and painted the sign of the cross on it. Within an hour the swelling disappeared and the woman went home "gladde and hole." St. Bartholomew's seems to have been the first hospital to have had a collector. This was Rahere's friend Alfune, who went around the district collecting money towards the upkeep of the hospital and also gifts in kind. He appears to have been very persistent, and there is a story of how his perseverance won over a hard-hearted butcher in the meat-market. For long this butcher refused to make any contributions but eventually he succumbed to Alfune's persuasive powers and gave him some meat to help to feed the patients.

The origin of St. Thomas's Hospital is not so clear as that of St. Bartholomew's. There was probably an infirmary attached to the priory of St. Mary Overie, which is now Southwark Cathedral, before the murder of Thomas Becket. When he was canonised in 1173 many hospitals were dedicated to him, for he was believed to have great healing powers. The Southwark hospital was destroyed by fire in 1212, but, largely through the efforts of the Bishop of Winchester, a new St. Thomas's Hospital was constructed in Borough High Street, where it remained until it was moved to its present site in the second half of the nineteenth century.

In the Middle Ages St. Bartholomew's and St. Thomas's Hospitals were not regarded as being of greater importance than a large number of others; their high place in the hospitals of

England only came much later, when for a long time they were almost the only hospitals in the whole country. Here only a few of the medieval establishments can be mentioned.

In 1141 some monks built the hospital of St. Bartholomew at Buckland by Dover, in Kent. Their work met with the approval of the Archbishop of Canterbury, who issued an appeal for help for "the hospital house of Dover, which two brethren, Osbern and Godwin, are diligently building for the reception of the poor and strangers." This hospital was used largely by lepers, who, because they were seldom cured, usually became permanent inmates. It was probably for this reason that there was a rule of the hospital that no leper could be admitted unless the other sufferers from leprosy already in the hospital gave their consent. This measure helped to maintain peace within the hospital. On admission the leper was required to take the following oath:

"I, —————, do promise before God and St. Bartholomew and all saints, that to the best of my power I will be faithful and useful to the hospital . . . obedient to my superior and have love to my brethren and sisters. I will be sober and chaste of body; and a moiety of the goods I shall die possessed of shall belong to the house. I will pray for the peace of the church and realm of England, and for the king and queen, and for the prior and convent of St. Martin, and for the burgesses of Dover on sea and land, and especially for all our benefactors, living and dead."

Following this vow, the leper was sprinkled with holy water and taken to the altar, where he knelt to receive the warden's blessing. It will thus be seen that to become a patient in a leper hospital was regarded as almost like entering a monastery. The Buckland hospital appears to have been very particular about the type of leper admitted, for not only did prospective patients have to meet with the approval of the existing inmates, but they also had to pay one hundred shillings, so that only a fairly wealthy leper, or one with well-to-do friends or relatives, could gain admission. The rules which governed the behaviour of the patients were also strict; for example, they were forbidden to engage in trade or usury. They had to say two hundred *Pater-nosters* and *Aves* during the hours of daylight and then during the night they were wakened by the dormitory bell and had to sit erect in bed and say another two hundred! The hospital at Buckland was one of those which held an annual fair in order to raise funds.

The foundation by King Athelstan of St. Peter's Hospital in York has already been mentioned. During the twelfth century it was destroyed by fire, but it was reconstructed as St. Leonard's Hospital by King Stephen. In addition to being a hospital and almshouse, it was also a children's home. Death in childbirth was far more common than it is now, and when this happened in the hospital the child was often kept there until he reached an age when he could go out into the world. At one time during the thirteenth century there were twenty-three boys at St. Leonard's. They had a woman in charge of them, and two schoolmasters were employed to teach grammar and music to them and the thirty choristers. In addition to the twenty-three child inmates there were 224 sick and poor; this made St. Leonard's the largest hospital in the country. Besides the schoolmasters, the staff included cooks, bakers, brewers, smiths, carters, a ferrywoman, boatmen, and sixteen male and female servants. There were also a number of "brothers" and "sisters." It seems that not all of these were actual workers; some lived in part of the hospital set aside for them and were provided with the necessities of life, being in effect almshouse inmates. Apparently there was a woman with a rank corresponding to that of matron, for at one time the principal sister was known as Matilda *la hus-wyf* and in 1416 a benefactor left money for the staff and inmates and directed that it should be distributed by Alice *materfamilias*. As in most of the medieval hospitals, religion played an important part. There were three chapels and each brother had to study at his desk in the cloister several times daily. St. Leonard's was one of the hospitals which provided food for any poor people who came to the gate; loaves and fishes were distributed to them daily and they were given a special dinner on Sundays. Hospitals were usually allowed to obtain wood for fuel from the nearby forests; Henry III gave St. Leonard's permission "to take what they need in the forest of Yorkshire for building and burning, and also of herbage and pasture for flocks and anything needful for their ease." The hospital was also allowed to collect a tax known as "Petercorn" or the "thraves of St. Leonard." It is not certain whether a thrave consisted of twelve, twenty or twenty-four sheaves of corn, but the hospital collected the appropriate number from every plough working in Cumberland, Westmorland, Lancashire and York-shire—the area which was under the episcopal jurisdiction of the Archbishop of York. In prosperous times the thraves ensured the hospital a good income; in the year 1369–70 its receipts amounted to £1,369, while its expenditure was only £938. When there was war or plague or famine, however, the hospital suffered; in 1409 the income fell to £546. At one time the master raised money by pawning the hospital chalices and ornaments—a step which met with strong disapproval from the patients, who submitted a petition to the king about the matter.

St. John's Hospital at Oxford was founded about 1180 and re-founded in 1233 by Henry III "that therein infirm people and strangers might receive remedy of their health and necessity." It was one of the few hospitals where the staff had the privilege of electing the master; in most hospitals he was appointed by the patron. The master of St. John's was always one of the three Augustinian chaplains who, with six lay-brothers and six sisters, formed the staff, although there were also, of course, a number of artisans and farm-workers employed. The strong religious ties of the hospitals sometimes led to disputes between Church and State; this happened at St. John's. Henry III declared that the Bishop of Lincoln had no right to carry out a visitation of the hospital and the bishop retaliated by refusing to consecrate a burial-ground there. The king appealed to the Pope, who directed that the bishop must provide a burial-ground. Not all monarchs regarded it as their duty to maintain the rights of the hospitals; some kings looked upon them as places where their servants should be maintained in old age or where board and lodging should be provided for their officials as they travelled about the country. Thus Edward II ordered St. John's to admit his chaplain and the chaplain's clerk and provide them with food, clothing, shoe-leather and wood.

Sometimes the hospital buildings were of stone, but some, such as those at Harbledown, were of wood, and this frequently led to destruction or severe damage by fire. There are a few con-temporary illustrations, mostly on seals, which show that hos-pitals were often church-like in appearance. From its seal we know that St. John's Hospital at Stafford had triple-lancet win-dows surmounted by trefoils. Written descriptions of medieval hospitals are even rarer than pictures of them, and seldom go into any great detail. There is a twelfth-century account of the build-ing of St. Bartholomew's in London, Matthew Paris left brief descriptions of three other London hospitals, and a Canterbury monk wrote descriptions of the two hospitals erected by Arch-bishop Lanfranc. Sometimes it seems that existing buildings were converted into hospitals. After so many centuries very few remains of the medieval hospitals exist. Some of the Norman work of St. John's Hospital at Canterbury, which was founded by Lan-franc in 1084, can still be seen. There are ruins of the infirmary hall and the chapel of St. Leonard's Hospital of York. Oriel College at Oxford owns the chapel of the leper hospital which was built about 1200; it adjoins the College sports ground and is now used as a church by Russians living in Oxford. The Ministry of Works has restored the Maison Dieu at Ospringe in Kent, and it is now open to the public, but this is a half-timbered house built on the site of an earlier hospital. There are small remains of a number of other hospitals in various parts of the country, but they are seldom sufficient to give much idea of the appearance of the complete buildings.

From the various sources available it can be gathered that the main gateway was often surmounted by a tower. Sometimes there was a kind of porch or almonry attached to the gate, where food and drink were distributed to wayfarers who did not re-quire admission to the hospital. This practice is still continued at

St. Cross' Hospital, Winchester, where bread and ale are issued to all who call at the gate—although those seeking these alms are no longer destitute vagrants, but fairly well-to-do tourists. The dining-hall or refectory of the larger hospitals was often a very fine building. Some of these halls had minstrels' galleries; others had a small loft where one of the brethren sat and read to the inmates while they were having their meals. One room sufficed for the small amount of office work that had to be done in those days; it was known as the chapter-house or the audit-room. Nearly all hospitals had a chapel; sometimes this was at the eastern end of the great hall, while in other cases it was a separate building. In some hospitals it was the practice to accommodate the sick in the great hall, as near as possible to the chapel, so that they could hear mass and take part in the services. Sometimes the hall, or part of it, was divided into small cubicles by means of screens. Often the chapels were remarkably fine buildings, even though they were intended to be used only by the inmates and staff of the hospitals. Separate accommodation was provided for the staff, who lived as a community. In the earliest hospitals the warden or master had to be one of this community and take his meals with the rest of the staff, but gradually he became more and more separated from them, until in the later establishments he was provided with a house of his own.

The master was often a priest, but seldom a physician, although he usually had some knowledge of medicine. In the case of leper hospitals, he was sometimes himself a leper. Usually he was appointed by the patron of the hospital, but the brethren of St. Leonard's, Lancaster, elected one of themselves as master. We know from documents that still exist that a very high standard of conduct was expected of the senior officers of the medieval hospitals. The master of London's Savoy Hospital had to be "mercifull, beningne and louyng to the poore, and not skoymys [squeamish] or lothesome to uisite theym or to be among theym." The master at Wells must be "circumspect and expert in spiritual and temporal things, and free from all infamous vice." At Heytesbury in Wiltshire the master was forbidden to visit the ale-house, go hunting, or play cards or handball. He must never be away from the hospital at night, and any absences during the daytime must only be of short duration, and besides conducting the services in the hospital chapel he had also to preach at some of those in the parish church and to act as master of the village school.

The "brothers" and "sisters" on the hospital staff were sometimes priests or monks and sometimes laymen. Not all of them were expected to assist in the work of the hospital; some were regarded as almshouse inmates and provided with food and clothing without being called upon to perform any duties. At Lechlade in Wiltshire only two of the brothers had to attend to the sick. In most hospitals one of the brethren held the office of proctor; it was his duty to collect alms. There is one instance of a woman being appointed to do this work. The sisters nursed the sick or carried out work in the household. Some women occupied high positions in the hospital, for, as stated previously, St. Leonard's at York had a *materfamilias*, who presumably corresponded to the modern matron. In addition to the brothers and sisters, there were paid employees who had to wait upon both the sick and the staff.

Naturally we know little of any particular patients, for the keeping of detailed medical records is a fairly modern development. It is indeed surprising to find that any of the patients of seven or eight hundred years ago are known to us by name, yet there are a number of these. The earliest was Orm, who lived near Whitby. We are told that he was a "good man and a just, but he was a leper." The abbot therefore built a little hospital especially for him and provided him with food for the rest of his life. This is one of several instances of hospitals being founded for particular individuals. There are records of kings sending faithful servants or others who found royal favour to hospitals for treatment or maintenance. Henry III ordered the hospital at Ospringe to receive Helen, a blind woman, as a sister. Veterans of the wars with France and Scotland were often sent to hospitals by royal command. The monarchs also frequently ordered hospitals to care for converted Jews, who were legally wards of the sovereign.

The hospital inmates of whom most is known are those who were supposed to have been the subject of miraculous cures, but in all the stories of these it is difficult to distinguish fact from fiction. The chronicles of St. Bartholomew's Hospital in London contain a number of such tales, a few of which are related in the next chapter. The shrines of two saints, Godric of Finchale and Thomas of Canterbury, were particularly noted for the cures effected at them. Among those who ascribed their recovery to St. Thomas was John King, a monk of Taunton Priory, who became a leper and was admitted to the local lazar-house. He was an inmate for more than a year and then went on a pilgrimage to Canterbury. He returned completely cured and seems to have spent the rest of his days gathering alms for his former fellow-inmates. To St. Godric was attributed the even more remarkable cure of a leper girl. She lived at Haughton-le-Skerne in Yorkshire with her widowed mother. The mother married again and the girl was so ill-treated by her stepfather that she sought the aid of the local priest, who arranged for her to be admitted to a nearby leper hospital. There she stayed for three years, during which her condition gradually became worse. Her mother took her to St. Godric's shrine three times, and on the third occasion the girl was completely cured. The sheriff and the priest both attested to the truth of this story.

Most hospitals had strict rules governing the conduct of both patients and staff. When the patients were admitted they were frequently required to take a solemn oath; that taken by those at St. Bartholomew's Hospital near Dover was set out earlier in this chapter. Sometimes the taking of the oath was not sufficient to secure admission. At Dover the sufferer had to pay 100 shillings—a considerable sum in those days—as well as giving gratuities of half a mark to the warden and half a mark to be shared between the brothers and sisters. On the other hand, the statutes of St. Nicholas's Hospital, York, forbade the granting of admission in return for the payment of money. As might be expected, the rules relating to lepers were aimed at preventing the spread of the disease. They were usually forbidden to enter ale-houses and taverns, although they were allowed outside the hospital provided they kept within a certain area. Sometimes these rules were applied to patients other than lepers. At Croydon the inmates were not go out of sight of the hospital, except to church.

The warden was responsible for maintaining order and discipline. Often he was required to hold a weekly chapter for the purpose of dealing with infringements of the regulations. He could punish by means of flogging and fasting, the stocks, and by imposing fines, and in very bad cases he could expel the offender. If a leper at Reading was guilty of any misbehaviour he was treated rather like a naughty child: during meals he was made to sit in the middle of the hall, feeding only on bread and water, while his share of the food and ale was distributed to the others. At St. Mary's, Chichester, a brother who concealed money from the warden had the cash hung about his neck, was flogged, and did penance for thirty days.

The strict rules of conduct and the equally severe regulations for the care of the soul made a medieval hospital almost like a monastery. Staff and patients all had to take part in religious services daily—matins, prime, tierce, mass, sext and none, all had to be observed. At St. James's Hospital, Chichester, the lepers had to rise at 1 a.m. and say the night office. At Sherburn in Durham those who were too ill to leave their beds had to sit up when they heard the bell and join in prayers; if they were too weak to do this, they had to lie still and pray.

It seems that as much—if not more—attention was paid to the spiritual well-being of a sick person as to the treatment of his ailments. Physicians were few and medical knowledge was limited. It appears to have been rare for the warden of a hospital to have been also a doctor, although we do know that the Duke of Lancaster made his own physician master of the hospital at Preston in 1355 and that at the end of the fourteenth century the warden of St. Nicholas's Hospital at Pontefract was "Louis the physician." Where there were monks on the hospital staff, these sometimes possessed a little knowledge of medicine. One of the things that the medical men were most ignorant about was the function of the human body. Their ignorance was due to the fact that the Church frowned upon the practice of anatomy.

There were a few men who had a wider knowledge of medicine and surgery because they had studied abroad, but it does not seem likely that they visited the hospitals in this country. Their patients were wealthy noblemen who could afford to pay the high fees demanded. One of these foreign-trained surgeons who specialised in rectal disorders wrote that for curing an anal fistula he always charged at least £68 13s. 4d., together with an annual pension of the same amount—and it must be borne in mind that this sum was worth far more then than it is today. Although this man could carry out operations for fistula and could treat cancer of the rectum, some of his methods savour of folklore and superstition. For example, when a man was brought to him with a badly diseased leg, he bathed it with warm white wine containing plantain juice, then placed on it a plaster of plantain, rhubarb, parsley, honey, rye meal and white of egg. This was followed by another plaster of black soap, sulphur and arsenic.

Although there was so little provision for medical attention, the hospital patients were well treated in other ways. The food, although plain by modern standards, was usually plentiful. At Sherburn every patient received a loaf and a gallon of beer daily; there was meat three times a week, and on the other days there were eggs, vegetables and cheese.

Fuel, consisting entirely of wood, was collected from the woods near the hospital. Usually this was done with the permission of the lord of the manor, but sometimes a royal decree was issued giving a hospital the right to gather wood; thus Henry III authorised St. John's Hospital at Oxford to obtain wood from Shotover.

The beds in the earliest hospitals consisted of pallets of straw, but it seems that before the end of the twelfth century there were wooden bedsteads, although often these were large and had to accommodate two or more patients. Even in those days some attention was paid to the cleanliness of the bedding. The warden of St. Thomas's Hospital, Canterbury, and his wife received an

annual payment of 46s. 8d. for "wasshyng of the bedds for poure
people," and one of the matters investigated at an inquiry at the
Savoy Hospital, London, in 1535 was "whether any poore man
do lie in any shetes unwasshed that any other lay in bifore."

Leper inmates had to wear distinctive clothing, usually consisting of a cloak, a hood, a coat and shoes. At Harbledown the
garments were russet in colour. The lepers were not allowed to
walk about barefooted; at Sherburn each inmate received an
annual payment of fourpence for shoes. The staff often wore a
monastic type of dress, a long black or brown robe. Sometimes
this bore a coloured badge.

Financially the hospitals were largely dependent on charity,
although some of them received regular payments from their
patrons, from the sovereign, or from the rents of land and houses.
Many early wills contain bequests to hospitals: Henry II's son,
William Longspée, bequeathed cows to the lepers in five hospitals,
while a humbler person bequeathed twelvepence to each of eight
hospitals.

A number of hospitals raised money by holding annual fairs.
Edward I granted St. James's Fair to the hospital "for maidens that
are leprous," which stood on the site of St. James's Palace. The
greatest fair of all, that of Sturbridge near Cambridge, was
authorised by a charter which King John granted in 1211 to the
lepers of the Hospital of St. Mary Magdalene.

Another source of revenue was the fees which patients of some
hospitals had to pay on admission. As mentioned earlier in this
chapter, in some cases these were quite large. An unpopular
means of ensuring that some members of the public contributed
towards the maintenance of the sick and the poor was the
granting to hospitals of the right to levy tolls on local produce.
Usually these tolls were in kind, as at Shrewsbury, where the
lepers took handfuls of corn and flour from the sacks in the market,
and at Carlisle, where every Sunday they had a pot of ale from
each brewhouse and a farthing loaf from every baker. Occasionally the tolls were in cash, as at Southampton, where the lepers of
St. Mary Magdalene's received a penny for every tun of wine

that was imported. Normally these tolls were only levied in the town or district where the hospital was situated, but sometimes they were imposed over a wide area. St. Leonard's Hospital at York collected a corn-tax as far away as Cumberland and Westmorland.

The total income obtained from fairs, admission fees and taxes was usually not very large, and most hospitals were chiefly dependent on charity. There were collecting-boxes at the hospital gates, and some of the hospitals sent one of their inmates on collecting missions. Sometimes these collectors, or proctors as they were called, sought alms not only in the immediate neighbourhood, but wandered all over the country. In order that people should know that they were genuine, they carried warrants issued by the king or the bishop. Pardons or indulgences were often granted to those who gave alms. Pilgrims were expected to make contributions to the hospitals where they stayed on their journeys; the collecting-box used at Harbledown is still preserved there. Even in those days there were in a few towns bodies somewhat similar to the modern Leagues of Friends. The members of the fraternity of St. John Baptist at Winchester each contributed one shilling annually to St. John's Hospital there.

Supervision of the administration of hospitals was the joint responsibility of king and bishop, both of whom were "visitors," although where the hospital was under royal patronage the bishop had no right of visitation. The king was usually visitor in name only, the actual duty being carried out by the chancellor. Sometimes special investigations were ordered to ensure that the hospital's rules were being obeyed, or to inquire into some serious allegations; a jury of local citizens was appointed to conduct such investigations.

Inquiries of this nature seem to have been frequently necessary, particularly during the fourteenth and fifteenth centuries, when the spirit of public service and religious zeal which had led to the founding of so many hospitals had grown weak. The situation was summed up by the statute for the reformation of hospitals which was enacted by Parliament in 1414; its preamble stated that many hospitals "be now for the most part decayed, and the goods and profits of the same, by divers persons, spiritual and temporal, withdrawn and spent to the use of others, whereby many men and women have died in great misery for default of aid, livelihood and succour."

Two factors were largely responsible for this state of affairs: abuse by the patrons and mismanagement by the wardens. The patrons often claimed the right of free lodging at the hospitals. Sometimes they arrived at a hospital with a whole retinue of retainers and demanded to be accommodated for the night. They sent their aged servants to the hospitals to be maintained there for the rest of their lives. Edward II actually declared that all the hospitals in the country were founded by his predecessors "for the admission of poor and weak persons, and especially of those in the king's service who were unable to work."

There are numerous records of mismanagement by wardens, and it seems that this was probably the chief factor contributing to the decline of the hospitals. A complaint was made in 1348 that the warden of St. Leonard's Hospital, Derby, "neglects the duties of the wardenship and has dissipated and consumed the goods and alienated the lands to the great decay of the hospital." Many wardens did not live at their hospitals or even visit them, and some were masters of several establishments. A Bishop of Winchester appointed his nephew, aged eighteen, as warden of the Portsmouth hospital and master of St. Cross Hospital, Winchester, and gave him an archdeaconry and two canonries in addition. Some wardens made fortunes by the sale of pensions and of goods belonging to their hospitals. The description given by Robert Copland in his poem *The hyeway to the Spytell house*, written about 1536, was true of far too many hospitals—

> For I haue sene at sondry hospytalles
> That many haue lyen dead without the walles
> And for lacke of socour have dyed wretchedly
> Unto your foundacyon I thynke contrary.
> Moche people resorte here and have lodgyng,
> But yet I maruell greatly of one thyng
> That in the night so many lodge without.

This mismanagement of hospitals, accompanied by a decline in the spirit of charity which had caused their foundation, led to the dissolution of many of them. Some of them were taken over by the colleges at Oxford and Cambridge, while others were used for various purposes, such as schools.

The lazar-houses had also been disappearing, but for a far better reason. The number of sufferers from the dread disease was slowly decreasing, so that few hospitals were required for them. However, as leprosy declined, venereal disease appeared, and many of the former lazar-houses came to be used for the treatment of sufferers from this. The lazar-houses just outside the City of London, including those at Knightsbridge, Mile End and Southwark, were among those whose use was changed in this way. Instead of being called lazar-houses, they came to be known as lock hospitals. The reason for this name is obscure; the most likely explanation is that it arose because the hospitals were usually near the city gates, and the patients were therefore locked out of the towns.

Henry VIII's statutes for the suppression of religious houses brought about the disappearance of many more hospitals, for most of them were connected with monasteries or closely associated with churches. St. Leonard's at York and St. Bartholomew's and St. Thomas's in London were among the hospitals that disappeared, although the first of these was replaced by a charity for thirty-one poor people.

A desperate situation was thus created, particularly in London, where the streets were filled by "sick and infirm poor men lying begging." There was now no religious or charitable spirit to lead to the alleviation of this state of affairs, but instead there developed a feeling of citizenship—an idea that the people of London must take action together in order to provide succour for the sick. The action they took was to get the Lord Mayor to make an urgent petition to the king for the re-foundation of St. Mary's, St. Bartholomew's and St. Thomas's Hospitals. The citizens asked Henry to grant them the governance of these hospitals, and said that if he acceded to this request "a greatter nombre of poore nedy sykke and indygent persons shalbe refresshed maynteyned comforted fownde heled and cured of theyre infirmities frankly and frely, by phisicions, surgeons, and appotycaryes." The petition was presented to the king in 1538, but six years elapsed before he deigned to reply. Then he issued letters-patent authorising the refoundation of St. Bartholomew's, and decreeing that it should be known as "The House of the Poor in West Smithfield of the foundation of King Henry VIII." By an Act of Common Council it was endowed with five hundred marks annually. The citizens raised a similar sum each year and also met the expense of repairing the hospital so that it could be opened for one hundred patients.

In the same year St. Mary's of Bethlehem became City property and was used as a hospital for the insane and in 1551 Edward VI issued letters-patent authorising the citizens to repair St. Thomas's Hospital, which they had purchased. It was re-opened with 260 beds. Two years later a report by the Bishop of London and the Lord Mayor led Edward to authorise the foundation of two more hospitals—Christ's Hospital for orphans and Bridewell for the correction of idle vagabonds. Thus it was that a spirit of civic responsibility led to the provision of hospitals to replace those founded as acts of religious charity. Because Henry VIII and Edward VI could claim to have refounded these five hospitals— although the prime movers in their re-opening were really the citizens of London—they were known as Royal Hospitals.

Even in the sixteenth century one man had visions of an ideal hospital service. In his *Utopia* the far-seeing statesman Sir Thomas More wrote—

> But first and chiefly of all, in respect of the sycke that be cured in the hospitalles. For in the circuit of the citie a little without the walls they have four hospitalles so big, so wide, so ample and so large that they may seem four little towns; which were devised of that bigness, partly to the intent the sycke, be they never so many in number, should not lie in throng or straight, and therefore uneasily or incommodiously; and partly that they which were taken and holden with contagious diseases such as would by infection to crape from one to another might be laid apart from the company of the residue. These hospitalles be so well appointed and with all things

necessary to health so furnished; and moreover so diligent attendance through the continual presence of cunning physicians is given, that though no man be sent thither against his will, yet notwithstanding there is no sick person in all the citie that had not rather lie there than in his own house.

In Henry VIII's reign there was some recognition of the importance of the medical profession. In 1518 the Royal College of Physicians had been founded. This was followed in 1540 by the establishment of the United Barber-Surgeons' Company, and in 1546 the first Regius Professor of Medicine was appointed at Cambridge.

CHAPTER II

ST. BARTHOLOMEW'S

FOR nearly two centuries after their refoundation St. Bartholomew's and St. Thomas's were the only important hospitals for the sick in the whole of England; the three other Royal Hospitals were really specialist establishments, since one was a house of correction and the other two were for insane people and orphans. This lack of hospitals has not been satisfactorily explained, for although the great religious impulse of the Middle Ages had waned, there was still an urge to perform charitable works. Yet this urge found its outlet chiefly in the foundation of alms-houses and schools. Why it never led people to establish hospitals is a mystery.

The few small hospitals which existed in the provinces probably did as much harm as good. The nurses for the most part were ignorant and often dirty, and if a patient recovered it was not usually due to the care he received but because his constitution was sufficiently strong to withstand the rough treatment. Consequently a sick person preferred to be nursed at home, and people only went to hospital when poverty or lack of friends absolutely forced them to do so. A patient often had to share a bed with at least one other person; the wards were never properly cleaned; and infectious patients were not isolated.

People suffering from the various forms of plague then prevalent were not admitted to the hospitals. For them, many towns provided small pest-houses. These were usually on the outskirts of the urban area or, like that which still exists at Odiham in Hampshire, on the edge of the churchyard, so that when an inmate died those who buried him could do so quickly and with as little trouble as possible. For a considerable time there was only one pest-house for the whole of the City of London; this was in St. Giles's, Cripplegate. Westminster had its own pest-house in Tothill Fields.

The foundation and re-foundation of St. Bartholomew's and St. Thomas's have already been briefly described, but their importance during the sixteenth and seventeenth centuries warrants a closer study of these two hospitals.

When Rahere founded St. Bartholomew's in 1123 he directed that it should have a master, eight brethren and four sisters. The master was usually a priest and three of the brethren were chaplains. The master should have "a servant fit for his place, who is to stay continuously in the infirmary and wait upon the sick with diligence and care in all gentleness." This servant was to prepare the patients' food, "show their water to the physician, and take a careful note of how they ought to diet themselves."

In the rules which were issued for the conduct of the hospital, it was made clear that the patients were the first consideration. Nevertheless, the accommodation for them provided little in the way of bodily comforts. They probably had to sleep in the same manner as the brethren—on rugs upon the floor. Gradually improvements were made: first, wooden bedsteads were provided, and then curtains were hung around them. The standard of cleanliness in those days was not very high, and there was one member of the staff whose job it was to keep the bedding free from bugs.

Some patients were, of course, financially better off than others. There were, indeed, a few who were equivalent to paying patients because while they were in the hospital they paid for the food and the treatment which they received.

The four sisters were nuns of the Augustinian order and devoted their whole lives to the service of the hospital. Some of them seem to have possessed property, for their wills contained bequests to the hospital. They wore grey tunics; the rule regarding these said that they must not reach lower than the ankles. They all slept in a dormitory, and had their meals in a refectory, where they shared their daily rations of seven loaves, half a flagon of ale and a dish of cooked food.

We have no definite knowledge of the medical and surgical treatment given to patients. Only those whose cures were miraculous received any place in the hospital's archives, and, as stated previously, it is not known to what extent the stories about them are true. As examples of these tales, we may take the cures of Wolmer and Adwyne.

Wolmer was well known to Londoners; for thirty years he begged for alms daily in old St. Paul's Cathedral. He was so badly deformed that he could move about only by dragging himself along on all fours. Then, when Rahere founded St. Bartholomew's, Wolmer's friends took him to the new hospital. Apparently he received no treatment, but was merely placed before the altar in the church. Yet this was sufficient to effect a cure, for "by and by euery crokidness of his body a litill and litill losid," until "all his membris yn naturale ordir was disposid."

Adwyne's cure took a little longer. He was a carpenter from Suffolk. Like Wolmer, he was terribly deformed. He heard of some of the miraculous cures wrought at St. Bartholomew's, and determined to make the journey to London. He travelled there by sea, and became a patient in the hospital. Gradually he regained the use of his hands, and was able to make small things like distaffs and weights, and then slowly his whole body was cured and he was able to exercise his trade of carpentry again. No doubt to Adwyne and his friends the recovery of the use of his limbs seemed miraculous, but a more realistic modern writer has suggested that he suffered from rheumatism and that this was cured by a long course of graduated exercises!

More reliable accounts of the medical and surgical treatment which were probably given at the hospital are contained in the *Breviarium Bartholomei* by John Mirfield, which was published in 1387. It is not certain that Mirfield actually worked at the hospital, but there seems little doubt that some of the treatments he described he had seen in use there. As an example, we may take the method of dealing with rheumatism. Olive oil had to be placed in a clean vessel by the pharmacist, who made the sign of the cross and said two prayers. Then the vessel was put over a fire and allowed to remain there while part of a certain psalm, the

Gloria, and two prayers were recited seven times. After all this had been done, the heated olive oil was applied to the affected part. It has been suggested that the recitation of the psalm and prayers was a means of timing the heating of the oil, for in those days there were few clocks, and watches were non-existent.

It is not until after the re-foundation of the hospital that we find any record of trained medical men on the staff. Three surgeons were appointed in 1549 and a physician in 1568. Some years later there were four surgeons and four physicians, and these numbers remained unchanged until 1895, although there were also assistant surgeons and assistant physicians.

One of the first surgeons appointed at the hospital was Thomas Vicary. In 1548 he wrote a book called *A Treasure for Englishmen, containing the Anatomie of Man's Body*; this was the earliest English textbook of anatomy. Vicary was the first Master of the newly-formed Barber-Surgeons' Company. Until 1540 there was often trouble between the surgeons, most of whom had received a fairly good education and training, and the barbers, who acted as the general practitioners of the time, drawing teeth and carrying out minor surgery. When they became united in one company, the barbers agreed to restrict their surgery to dentistry, and the surgeons undertook to cease to practise as barbers. By an Act of Parliament the new company was allowed to fine unlicensed practitioners in London and to have the bodies of four executed criminals each year for dissection. The company aimed to raise the status of surgery; to this end lectures and demonstrations were arranged which all members had to attend. The surgeons were forbidden to administer medicines for internal disorders; this was the province of the physicians, who were not allowed to carry out operations, even such simple ones as blood-letting.

Nevertheless, there were many who practised medicine without any qualifications or training whatsoever. Their victims were often later taken to hospital, in the hope that the physicians and surgeons there could undo the work of the quacks. Thomas Gale, who was Serjeant-Surgeon to Queen Elizabeth, has left an account of what happened—

In the year 1562 I did see in the two hospitals in London called
St. Thomas' Hospital and St. Bartholomew's Hospital to the number three hundred and odd poor people that were diseased of sore
legs, sore arms, feet and hands, with other parts of the body, so sore
infected that a hundred and twenty of them could never be recovered
without loss of a leg or of an arm, a foot or a hand, fingers or toes,
or else their limbs crooked so that they were either maimed or else
undone for ever. All these were brought to this mischief by witches,
by women, by counterfeit rogues that take upon them to use the
art, not only of robbing them of their money but of their limbs and
perpetual health. And I, with certain others, diligently examining
these poor people, how they came by their grievous hurts and who
were their chirurgeons that looked unto them and they confessed
that they were either witches, which did promise by charms to
make them whole, or else some women which would make them
whole with herbs and suchlike things, or else some vagabond rascal
which runneth from one country to another promising unto them
health only to deceive them of their money.

Once a week all the doctors at St. Bartholomew's made a tour
of the wards together, led by the physician and the surgeon who
had examined the new patients on the preceding admission day.
They were accompanied by members of the staff carrying the
ward books, in which the names of all the patients were written.
The physicians sat down in each ward and the patients were
brought to them. After each one had been examined, the treatment for him was written in the book. When all the patients in
the ward had been dealt with, the book was taken to the apothecary and, unless they were too ill to do so, the patients had to go
to him and collect their medicine. It seems that the physicians
were regarded as being far superior to the surgeons, for the apothecary was not allowed to make up any medicine for them unless
the prescription was countersigned by a physician.

There is one description of an amputation carried out at the
hospital by John Woodall, a surgeon who lived from 1569 to
1643. He wrote—

The patient was a certain poor maid or woman servant in London,
named Ellen French, of whom there were made books and ballads,
that were sung about the streets of her, namely, that whereas the

said maid or servant was given to pilfering, and being accused thereof by her master and mistress, used to curse and swear and with words of execration to wish, that if she had committed the crime she stood accused of, that then her legs and hands might rot off, the which thing accordingly, no doubt by the providence of God, came to pass, as a judgment upon her, namely that both her legs almost to the gartering place, with parts of seven of her fingers did rot off, the which wretched woman nevertheless, being referred to me in Saint Bartholomew's Hospital to be cured, by God's mercy and permission, I healed her perfectly, by cutting off both her sphacelated [i.e. gangrenous] legs in the mortified parts with also parts of her seven fingers, as is said, all in one morning without pain, terror or any loss of blood unto her, in the taking them off, and made her perfectly whole in a very short time, namely within three months, so merciful is God unto us vile creatures, when we are most unworthy of such his mercies.[1]

The same surgeon gave the following instructions for an amputation—

The amputation once resolved upon and all things ready for the work, let the Surgeon with all his assistances and friends not forget before the beginning of the work heartily to call upon God for a blessing upon their endeavours, and let the patient the day before have notice given him that he may also take time to prepare himself with true resolution of soul and body to undergo the work, as being never performed without danger of death, which done, then let the Surgeon prepare himself also with his helpers, namely at the least five persons besides himself, as for example, one to sit behind the patient to hold him, a second for a holder, who by the surgeon must be instructed to stand fast before him and to bestride the limb to be amputated and to hold the limb; and a third to hold and stay the lower end of the diseased member to be taken off; a fourth to receive and bring back the sharp instruments; a fifth, to attend the Artist and deliver to him his needles and buttons, restrictive rollers, bolsters, bladder and so soon as possibly may be to stay with the palm of his hand the medicines applied to the end of the amputated stump that being the duty of the fifth helper and the sixth is the Artist himself that dismembereth. Six and not fewer are the least for the work of taking off a member proceeding by a wound by Gun-shot, done in the lacerated not totally mortified part. But for the taking off of a member in the mortified part three persons as assistants may

[1] *The Surgeon's Mate* by John Woodall (1639).

serve, or two for the need, namely one to hold the upper part, the other the lower end. Let the Surgeon have ready for instruments a fit amputating Cerra [saw], a Catlin [amputating knife], and a good small incision knife, a good pair of strong scissors and three or four cauterising instruments. Let one of the assistants take the upper part of the member, holding it in both hands reasonably fast and steady. I mean the whole part thereof somewhat near unto the unsound part and let the other helper hold the other part. I mean the putrid part to be abscissed [amputated] in his hand whilst the Surgeon first by circumcising divide the putrid flesh from the bone doing it somewhat near the quick part but not too near it, about an inch full from the quick part that with the Cerra he may come without fear to divide the bone or bones asunder where he is sure they are sphacelated not touching any quick part at all with his sharp instruments which he may observe the certainer to do, if with a Needle he enquire cautiously. Let him also divide betwixt the bones the parts there being lest by lacerating or tearing with the teeth of the Cerra he offend, which done let the Artist amputate the bones.[1]

The sisters continued to play an important part in the work of the hospital. In 1544 their number was increased to five, and in 1551 a further seven were appointed. Each of them received an annual grant of six yards of cloth, valued at 22s. 6d. a yard, from which to make their uniform; the colour of this was changed from grey to blue. One of them acted as matron; amongst her duties she had to see that the other sisters did not come out of the women's ward after 7 p.m. in winter or 9 p.m. in summer "except for some great and special cause as the present danger of death or needful succour of some poor person." The regulations governing the sisters' conduct enjoined them, amongst other things, to "avoid and shun the conversation and company of all men," unless this was absolutely necessary in the course of their duty.

The matron did not live in the common dormitory with the sisters, but occupied a separate house, where, until the eighteenth century, she had the strange privilege of augmenting her wages by selling beer! Her salary was £3 5s. 8d. a year, while the sisters received only £2 a year.

[1] *The Surgeon's Mate* by John Woodall (1639).

It is not known when night nurses were first employed. They certainly existed in the middle of the eighteenth century, although they were called "watchers." Apparently they worked only when circumstances warranted it, for they lived outside the hospital and were called in when they were required.

After the hospital's re-foundation its administration was placed in the hands of a master and four chaplains, but they proved to be so incompetent that in 1547 the City authorities decided to make sweeping changes. A Court of Governors was appointed; its members consisted of men belonging to the Court of Aldermen and the Common Council and also of some persons who had made gifts to the hospital. The Lord Mayor presided over the Court of Governors. Their chief official, whose appointment was permanent, was called the Treasurer.

There was also an officer known as the hospitaller, who was a person in holy orders. Besides being responsible for the religious ministration of the hospital he looked after the food supplies and dealt with the patients' property. Religious observances continued to form an important part of the patients' daily routine. There was a morning service at 8 a.m., an afternoon service at 4 p.m. and evensong three hours later. They were quite lengthy services: that in the morning consisted of prayers and responses, two psalms, an anthem, another psalm, a lesson, the Benedicite, the Kyrie and the Creed, and ended with more prayers and responses. The hospitaller must have been quite a busy man, yet he somehow managed to do some of the doctors' work as well, for he sometimes claimed payments for setting bones and joints!

The date of the founding of the medical school at St. Bartholomew's is unknown. It seems to have been a gradual development. From 1540 to 1745 all surgeons practising in London or within seven miles of the city had to be licensed with the Barber-Surgeons' Company. Licences were granted only to men who had served a seven years' apprenticeship. The apprentice or his father had to pay fees to the Company and to the surgeon with whom he served. The surgeons at the hospital could offer better opportunities than those working elsewhere, and so they were able to take their pick of the apprentices and also charge higher fees. It became the practice for an apprentice to be appointed to fill his master's post when a surgeon retired or died, and so for many years the surgical staff lacked experience of work and ideas from outside the hospital. This system continued until the eighteen-thirties.

It is fortunate that the journals of the governors' meetings have been preserved from the very first occasion on which they gathered to transact business. This was on 4th October 1549. It must have been a very short meeting, for the minutes consist of only one sentence—

> At the assemble yn the persons of Mr. Dobbs, Mr. Whyt, Mr. Lyon, Aldermen: Mr. Clarke, Mr. Vycars, Mr. Morton and John Blundell, thes thynges were don:
> The master coke, the butlar, the porter the viii bedelles and the matrone shall have for ther wynter lyuerys to Marche russett frysse for ther cottes and for a pettycotte.

(The "viii bedelles" were the eight beadles who had been on the hospital's establishment since 1546. Their duty was to go around London and bring to the hospital any sick, aged and impotent people whom they found.)

The journals make very interesting reading, besides revealing a great deal about the work and administration of the hospital through the centuries, as the following items show—

1551   A gift of three gurds of turpentine was reported.
1554   A butcher agreed to supply beef and mutton at 1d. a pound.
1555   The surgeons requested the provision of a hot house for the poor to sweat in.
1557   The brewer was paid 3s. 2d. for every barrel of beer.
1558   The matron was allowed fresh soap for washing her clothes. (Before this, she had to use wood ashes.)
1568   On a day in March the governors met at 7 a.m. to make a general view of the hospital buildings and land.
1571   In November a man wanted to have his leg amputated, but the governors decided that the time of the year was

unsuitable and sent him to a lazar-house until the following spring. (From this entry it appears that the final decision as to whether an operation should be performed rested with the governors, and not with the surgeons.)

1577   William Story, the guide of the lazar-house at Highgate, was paid 13s. 4d. for the expenses he incurred when he caused the leg of a woman patient to be cut off.

1580   The payment to the sisters for board wages was raised from 16d. to 18d. a week. (In addition to this they received a yearly stipend of 40s.)

1587   The steward was given permission to get married.

1612   The hospitaller complained that because of the increased cost of living his salary of £10 a year was insufficient. It was raised to £15.

1634   The governors decided not to attend the corpse of Alderman Sir Martin Lumley because he had left no legacy to the hospital.

1647   Two soldiers complained that a sister in Soldiers' Ward had made reviling speeches against Sir Thomas Fairfax; she had also used provoking language to the patients and denied them things with which they should have been provided. The sister was suspended "until further consideration."

1649   A patient named Katherine Shaw wanted to bring her child into the hospital when she was admitted. She was allowed to do this and the governors each gave a shilling from their own purses to pay for the child's maintenance.

1651   The treasurer was ordered to pay ten shillings for a steel instrument for a child who was crooked.

1652   A widow was provided with a wooden leg at a cost of three shillings.

1653   It was decided that the porter should have a cloth gown every three years and should carry a staff tipped with silver and decorated with the arms of the hospital.

1654   Mary Kidder, the buttery woman, was dismissed for marrying.

1655   It was ordered "That the Cellar for stronge beare in this hospitall shalbe shutt upp every Sabbothday untill fiue of the clock in the afternoon, and then not to continue open longer than one hower, and alsoe that dureing that hower noe person or persons bee suffered to drink therein but only to fetch what beare or ale they shall want into their severall wards."

1659   Francis Worts was employed for the cure of scald heads. (This term covered eczema of the scalp and other ailments affecting the head.)

1669   It was decided that any governor who arrived late at a meeting or left before its business was completed should put a shilling in the poor box.

1675   A deficiency of £243 11s. 6d. was discovered in the accounts. The committee were unable to find out how this had occurred, but decided that the clerk's book-keeping system was unsatisfactory and ordered him to alter it.

1681   The apothecary reported that one hundred patients required mutton diet and broth in the spring and the autumn. The mutton provided by the matron was not sufficient and she was ordered to ensure that each patient had a pint of broth and a mutton chop.

1684   The cook was dismissed for refusing to receive the Sacrament according to the usage of the Church of England.

1685   Mr. Mollins was too ill to operate for stone and appointed a stranger to perform the operation without first getting permission for this arrangement. The governors ordered that no stranger should be nominated to cutting for the stone without leave.

1687   The following new diet table was approved—

> *Sunday*   10 ounces of Wheaten Bread
> 6 ounces of Beefe boyled without bones
> 1 pint and a halfe of Beef Broth

	1 pint of Ale Cawdell
	3 pints of 6 shilling Beere.
Monday	10 ounces of Wheaten Bread
	1 pint of Milk Pottage
	6 ounces of Beefe.
	1½ pints of Beefe Broth
	3 pints of Beere.
Tuesday	10 ounces of Bread
	Halfe a pound of Boyled Mutton
	3 pints of Mutton Broth
	3 pints of Beere.
Wednesday	10 ounces of Bread
	4 ounces of Cheese
	2 ounces of Butter
	1 pint of Milk Pottage
	3 pints of Beere.
Thursday	The same allowance as Sunday
	1 pint of Rice Milke.
Friday	10 ounces of Bread
	1 pint of Sugar Soppes
	2 ounces of Cheese
	1 ounce of Butter
	1 pint of Water Gruell
	3 pints of Beere.
Saturday	The same allowance as Wednesday.

Each patient was also allowed sixpence a week.

1696 Because out-patients had become so numerous it was decided that none should be allowed to attend without a certificate of poverty.

1699 It was decided that a surgeon should be paid 6s. 8d. for every amputation. A regulation was made that no patient should have a limb amputated without the approval of the treasurer and governors and the concurrence of all the surgeons. The patient's friends must be notified of the operation.

The sister of Charity Ward was dismissed after admitting that she was a Roman Catholic.

1703 In October the bakers asked to be relieved from a contract they had made in April to supply bread at 7½d. per dozen, as this caused them loss. It was agreed to pay them 9½d. per dozen from Midsummer to Michaelmas.

1704 Elizabeth Bond offered to clear the beds and wards of bugs for 6s. per bed. The governors offered her 40s. to clear the sisters' room of bugs.

1707 It was decided that the room over the cellar where the matron sold beer and ale should be made into a ward.

1708 One hundred copies of a book called *The Practice of Piety*, by the Bishop of Bangor, were bought and given to patients.

1711 It was decided that patients who had not enough money to buy themselves necessaries should be allowed a sum not exceeding one shilling.

1712 James Jones, a joiner, agreed to clear the wards of bugs for an immediate payment of five guineas and a further payment of £5 at the end of the year.

1714 Orders were given that the stones taken from patients who were operated upon should be brought into the counting house and shown to the treasurer and governors, and then hung there. (This appears to have been the beginning of the pathological museum.)

1722 The physicians and surgeons made representations to the governors regarding the necessity for a dissecting room and for a hot and cold bath for the use of patients.

1723 Instructions were given for the whitewashing of the following wards: Long, Cloister, Charity, Soldier, Cutting and Mary.

1740 One hundred beds of "good stout Hamborough ticken filled with thirty pounds of best brown flocks and quilted" were purchased for 13s. 6d. each.

1744 It was decided that patients should forfeit their dinner on any Sunday or holiday if they did not go to church.

1752   Until this year patients who developed smallpox after admission were allowed to remain in the general wards. It was at last realised that this helped to spread the infection, and it was decided that a patient who became ill with smallpox should be removed immediately to a ward set aside for persons with this disease.

CHAPTER III

ST. THOMAS'S HOSPITAL

THE date when St. Thomas's Hospital was founded is not known. It may have been as early as 1106, when the Norman priory of St. Mary was built at Southwark. This was an Augustinian priory, and as the monks of this order paid special attention to the care of the sick it is fairly certain that they would allow travellers to use the infirmarium which was attached to the priory and was really intended only for members of the priory who fell ill. These travellers were numerous, for St. Mary's stood beside the main highway entering London from the south. It seems likely that gradually the infirmarium became more and more independent of the priory, although it remained subject to the control of the prior until it was rebuilt on a new site in Borough High Street in 1215 after being destroyed by fire. It may have changed its name to St. Thomas's in 1173, when Thomas Becket was canonised.

The new hospital was supervised by a master, whose staff consisted of four brethren and three sisters. In addition to these, there were, of course, a number of lay workers. From 1277 the brethren were allowed to elect the master. It was not a large hospital and probably never had more than forty beds, the number at the time of the Dissolution. At first the patients had to sleep on rushes or straw pallets. When beds were introduced each of them had to be shared between two or three patients, who wore no night clothes at all. From deeds now in the British Museum it is known that the hospital derived much of its income from the rents paid for land which it owned. Many gifts and bequests are also recorded.

In the early part of the fourteenth century the behaviour of the staff gave cause for complaint, although we do not know in what way they misbehaved. In 1323 the Bishop of Winchester reprimanded the master because of the irregular lives which the brethren and sisters were leading. He also told the master that he must have his meals with the brethren and sisters.

The Black Death had a serious effect upon the hospital's finances. The shortage of labourers meant that its income from the land was drastically reduced, while the plague caused a great increase in the number of patients. In 1357 the brethren asked the Pope to grant two years and eighty days' indulgence to everybody who assisted the hospital, but he declined to allow indulgences of more than half of this length.

While he was Mayor of London the famous Dick Whittington built a new ward for the hospital. A document written by a later mayor contains the following passage—

> Thomas Spetylle. And at that same place ys an ospytalyte for pore men and wymen, and that noble marchaunt, Rycharde Whytyngdon, made a newe chambyr with viii beddys for yong wymen that had done a-mysse in trust of good mendement. And he commaundyd thatt alle the thyngys that ben don in that chambyr shulde be kepte secrete with owte forthe, yn payne of lesyng of hyr levynge; for he wolde not shame no yonge women in noo wyse, for hit myght be cause of hyr lettyng [hindrance] of hyr maryage.

More building had to be carried out in 1507, for the hospital had become very dilapidated. The sum spent on the new buildings was £326, which was, of course, equivalent to a far larger amount in modern money.

In the reign of Henry VIII the hospital acquired a very bad reputation. In 1535 the king appointed Thomas Cromwell and two other commissioners to carry out a visitation of all churches and monasteries, including hospitals attached to them, but the man who actually made the inspections on their behalf in Kent, Sussex and Surrey was Richard Layton. St. Thomas's was the last place he visited, and before going there he wrote to Cromwell saying he would complete his work by inspecting the "bawdy" hospital of St. Thomas's in Southwark. The whole area around the hospital had for long had an unsavoury reputation, for it was noted for its "stews" or houses of ill fame. These were actually under the supervision of the Bishop of Winchester, who at one time leased them to the Mayor of London.

Layton's letter is not the only evidence that affairs at the hospital were not as they should have been. The following year a number of people complained that a poor woman in childbirth had been refused admission to the hospital and had died at the church door. They also said that the master kept a concubine in the hospital and that he sold the church plate.

When the suppression of all religious houses with an annual income of less than £200 was ordered, St. Thomas's escaped because its revenue had been assessed at £266 17s. 6d. Only a few years passed, however, before the larger religious establishments were treated in a similar manner and in 1540 the hospital and all its possessions were surrendered to the king. He ignored an appeal that the hospital should be handed over to the City authorities in order that "a great number of poore, needy, syke and indigent persones shall be refreshed, maynteyned and comforted; and also heled and cured of their infermities frankly and freely by physicians, surgeons and potycaries which shall have stipende and salarie only for that purpose."

It was not until 1551 that further petitions led Edward VI to grant the hospital and its possessions to the mayor, commonalty and citizens of London, with instructions that their revenues should be spent "in the maintenance of the sick and infirm poor." A court of thirty citizens was appointed to carry out these instructions and they decided that the hospital would have to care for the following—

Of ffatherles children	300
Of sore and sick psons	200
Of poore men overburdened with children	350
Of aged persons	400
Of decayed householders	650
Of ydell vagabondes	200

The court or committee had to obtain money to repair and equip the buildings before they could re-open the hospital. Collections were made among the people of London, who "gave franckly the worke was so generally well lyked." A treasurer was appointed with a number of officers to work under him—a hospitaller (whose annual salary was £10), a clerk (£10), a steward (£6 13s. 0d.), a butler (£5), a cook (£8) and six surgeons (£15 each). The hospital opened its doors once more in 1552 and 250 patients were admitted.

At first the three royal hospitals of St. Thomas's, Christ's and Bridewell were controlled by the same court of governors, who held their meetings at Christ's Hospital. It was soon found necessary to decentralise the administration, and from 1556 St. Thomas's had its own court, although until 1587 the governors continued to be elected at an annual ceremony at Christ's Hospital. As in the case of St. Bartholomew's, the minutes of the governors have been preserved right from the very first meeting.

This was held on 4th January 1556, when the governors directed that a "Book of the Government of the Hospital" should be drawn up. The Book shows that the Court of Governors had full control over the finances and property of the hospital and also over the admission of patients. There were three aldermen serving on the Court and the oldest of these was to be President. The other governors were referred to as almoners. Each year two aldermen and four almoners were to be appointed "to vew and peruse all suche Landes as apperteigne to the saide hosspitall."

At a meeting in the following month it was decided that the almoners should visit the hospital in rotation. Each tour of duty would last a week, during which the almoner would go to the hospital twice daily to inspect the food provided for dinner and supper and to "see the officers doth their duties according to their charges."

There is no mention of a matron in the list of officers who were to serve under the treasurer, but it appears that one was appointed, for in 1557 the minutes stated that "the goodman Waymond hathe admonyshyon that from henceforthe he entermeddle not in the matron's office his wyf, upon payn of heir discharg of her said office." Apparently the goodman ignored this "admonyshyon" with the result that Mrs. Waymond ceased to be matron and was replaced by Amyc Creade. The new matron brought trouble of another kind, for less than ten months after her appointment she "exhibited a bill of sartayne faults agaynst the susters." The governors investigated her complaints and found them to be "more of malice than of any grounde of trothe."

Until 1566 the medical staff consisted only of surgeons, but in that year a physician was appointed at a salary of £13 6s. 8d. per annum. The surgeons received £15 a year, but they considered this insufficient and in 1557 they applied for an increase, although it appears that this was not granted. We know little of the physicians' methods of treating the patients; our very limited knowledge is gained from such prescriptions as the following—

> A medicen for scalde heads:
> First take a pynte of Musterde, a pynte of strong Vynegre, a quarter of a lb. of Verdegrease, Two peneworth of oyle de spike, an ounce of peper fynly beaten. Put thereto a handful of sowte [i.e. salt]. Boyle them together and styre them well, put in an earthen pote and so use it.
> An oyntement to correct the same yf it fortune to breake out agayne. Take a lb. of barrow hogges grease well toyed with an handful of goose dunge with whyte ends and as much of shepes dunge, one penesworth of oyle spike, one peneworth of honye, ii oz. dimidium of peper, one oz. of stavesacre [a kind of larkspur] and when yt is boyled then streane it Thoroughe a Clothe. After the fyrst melicyn [?] Take Vynegre warme it and washe it. And so the Scorfe shall be taken away.

The physicians' knowledge of medicine was little, if any, better than the surgeons' knowledge of the human body. The Renaissance had brought some relaxation with regard to the practice of anatomy. Henry VIII had presented a charter to the Barber-Surgeons' Company, authorising them to license all surgeons in the London area and permitting them to have the bodies of four executed felons annually for dissection. But the practice was still frowned upon by many, including some doctors. Charles II's physician in ordinary was of the opinion that "anatomy is no further necessary to a surgeon than the knowledge of the nature of wood to a carpenter or of stone to a stone cutter."

As far as their bodily comforts was concerned, the patients do not appear to have been badly treated. By the end of the sixteenth century they had feather beds. The governors did all they could to ensure that the food was good, for when they entered into a contract for the supply of meat they specified that it must be the "best flesche except the neck and the bluddie meate." The patients also received a quart of beer daily. There was, however, one regulation which undoubtedly caused a great deal of unhappiness among some of them: no husband and wife were allowed in the hospital at the same time. If a married couple both came for treatment, the one whose condition was the more serious was permitted to remain while the other was sent away. The reason for this rule is not given; it was also applied to the staff, and the sisters were not even allowed to become engaged without the permission of the matron.

One of Henry VIII's last acts had been to abolish the stews of Southwark. However, this did not prevent loose women from continuing to frequent the neighbourhood, and in 1561 the governors forbade the admission of any woman with child, stating that the hospital was "a house erected for the relief of honest persons and not of harlottes."

Those patients who were able to do so were asked to pay a shilling a week for their maintenance and treatment. The same charge seems to have been made regardless of the disease from which the patient was suffering, except that if it was venereal disease he had to pay 20d. These fees were collected by the hospitaller as one of the numerous duties attached to his post. In addition, he had to read the service from the Prayer Book daily to the patients, administer the Sacrament to them, bury those who died in the hospital, allot new patients to the various surgeons, distribute fuel to the poor, issue lead tokens to those patients who were allowed to go out of the hospital so that they could show these tokens to the porters as an indication that they had permission to pass through the gates, collect the clothes of all men dying in the hospital and store them until the governors reached a decision regarding their disposal, and, in conjunction with the matron, report all offences to the governors. His salary for all this work was £10 a year and four pints of beer daily!

It seems that there were plenty of offences to be brought to the governors' notice, for they found it necessary to provide a whipping post "to ponish the sturdy and transgressors." Among those who transgressed and were whipped was one of the sisters; the incident is recorded in the minutes—

> It was agreed at this courte upon complainte made by thospitler and matrone of one Jone Thornton, one of the sisters, for misusing of her body contrarie unto the law of god, that the saide Jone Thornton, according unto her desarte, should have for her ponyshmente twelve stryppes well layde on.

As at St. Bartholomew's, there was difficulty in getting the patients to attend the religious services, and the same punishment was adopted—those who did not go to church forfeited their dinner. Even this was not sufficient to compel attendance, so the governors decreed that offenders should lose their supper as well.

Until 1566 the patients, the sisters and the other members of the staff were not forced to have the food provided for them. They were paid a boarding allowance and many of them used this to purchase food from outside the hospital. The governors put a stop to this practice by forbidding the porters, under pain of dismissal, to allow anybody to fetch food from outside, "in order that the profitte may growe to this house."

In 1561 there were 111 patients. It was then decreed that the number must not exceed one hundred, but this ruling was ignored, for it continued to increase steadily, and within eight years had reached 203. More than half of these were known as "dieters": they were the patients who were too poor to pay the charge of one shilling a week.

Although it seems that the patients had plenty of food, they certainly lacked warmth and light. Until 1587 there were no fires in the wards, and the only means of illuminating them during darkness was candles. These were made from the fat of the meat which was collected by the cook and handed over to the steward.

In the early part of the seventeenth century reversions to the surgeon's posts were often granted several years before they became vacant, so eagerly were they sought after. The hospitaller decided which of the surgeons should treat each case. It seems that there was no resident medical officer, although one or two of the doctors often lived near the hospital.

In 1605 the governors for the first time appointed one of those bodies which now play such an important part in hospital administration—a committee. This particular committee was not set up to consider a matter of any great importance, but merely to decide whether a brick wall should be built to replace a broken paling around the back yard. The patients were slipping out through the gap in the fence and buying beer!

There are several references in the minutes to special payments being made to surgeons for lithotomy, or "cutting for the stone," as it was called. The first of these references is in 1621, when Mr. James Molins, a surgeon, was paid "a fine of £10 for his extraordinary skill in cutting four of his patients for the stone." Two years later Mr. Molins was appointed to cut for stone both at St. Bartholomew's and St. Thomas's at an annual salary of £30. He also had to treat "the rupture or falling downe of the intestines or gutts into the codds by cutting."

In the same year the governors made a regulation regarding the way in which they should dress when attending meetings of the court. Any governor who sat in court without wearing a gown was to pay a fine of twelve pence.

Charles I seems to have been perturbed about the salaries of the medical staff, for in 1629 he sent a letter to the governors asking if the payments made to the doctors, the surgeons, and the apothecary were not too small. The apothecary's salary was raised from £45 to £60 a year, but from this he had to provide all the drugs. The medical men's pay was not increased until the following year, when the surgeons received £6 a year more and the physician £5. Previously the latter had received £25 and the former £30 each.

In 1634 the governors took action to restrict the number of patients admitted. At that time there were "300 and odd," and it was decided to limit the number to two hundred and forty in summer and two hundred and eighty in winter. Apparently patients were admitted when there were no beds for them, for the matron was instructed "not to place more patients than there are beds in any ward." No patient discharged as incurable was to be readmitted for the same complaint and "no patient with the fowle disease shall be admitted until there be roome in the fowle wards." This rule shows that it was the usual practice to segregate patients with "the fowle disease"—the seventeenth-century name for V.D.

In 1639 both the matron and the hospitaller were sent to gaol. The matron was in debt to the tune of over £100; she attributed this to the fact that for fifteen years she had received only 2s. 4d. a week for her food. It is not known what offence had been committed by the hospitaller. The governors made no attempt to get him released but they set up a committee to try to persuade the authorities to free the matron. The "persuasion" took the form of a payment of £50!

By this time the hospital had fourteen wards, each with a sister in charge. The total number of beds remained at two hundred and eighty. Most of the wards had biblical names, such as Jonas, Magdalen and Tobias, although there were also a King's Ward, a Queen's Ward, and a Nightlayers' Ward. Most of them had tiled floors, although within the next twenty years five of them were provided with deal floors.

During the seventeenth century the demand for drugs increased rapidly. It will be recalled that the cost of these had to be met by the apothecary out of his meagre salary of £60 a year. In 1636 there were complaints that the patients were not receiving the best medicines because of the smallness of the salary, and so it was increased to £100. Four years later this figure was doubled.

Lying-in cases were not allowed in the hospital. The responsibility for ensuring that this rule was observed was placed upon the matron. Each month she had to examine all the women patients suspected of being with child. If she failed to carry out this duty and a baby was born within the hospital, she had to pay for its maintenance.

About the middle of the century an important change was made in the hospital administration. The Governors' Court had been holding meetings three or four times a year. Now it seems that they felt that this was insufficient to deal with all the business and that a smaller body meeting more frequently would be more efficient. It was therefore decided to set up a standing committee of nineteen governors, who would meet fortnightly. This body, which came to be known as the Grand Committee, remained in existence for little more than a year. After that, various other committees were set up from time to time, usually to deal with special matters.

The hospital was affected by both the Great Plague and the Great Fire of London. Early in 1665, when the plague began, the governors decided to pay £20 to Edward Rice, who "had cured some officers and many patients of this disease, all the surgeons refusing to intermeddle therein." Because of the plague the governors did not meet again for more than a year.

Southwark, where the hospital stood, was not touched by the Great Fire of 1666, but a great deal of the property which belonged to the hospital elsewhere in London was destroyed. This led to a decrease of £600 a year in its revenue. Because of this the governors proposed to stop the admission of any more sick or wounded seamen—we were at that time at war with the Netherlands—but the naval authorities persuaded them to continue to take a few sailors. A rule was made, however, that these men must "take not tobacco in their bedds to the indangering of the house by fire."

Relations between members of the staff were sometimes not nearly as good as they ought to have been. In 1698 one of the surgeons was suspended because he assaulted a colleague. Unfortunately the cause of the quarrel is not stated in the minutes. The surgeon who was suspended was later reinstated, but the incident led to a rule that in future any officer who struck another within the precincts of the hospital would be expelled.

In 1699 forty-one rules for the governance of the hospital were enacted or re-enacted. Here are a few of the more interesting of them—

1. No patient was to be admitted more than once for the same disease.
2. No incurables or persons suffering from infectious diseases were to be admitted.
3. The patients were to have their wounds dressed by the surgeons before 10 a.m. in winter and 9 a.m. in summer.
4. The doctors and surgeons were to meet at 10 a.m. on Monday, Thursday and Saturday. On Saturday they had to walk through every ward together.
5. Some of the governors were to inspect the patients once a week without giving notice of their visit.
6. All staff and patients were to go to the chapel when the bell was rung.
7. No swearing or quarrelling was allowed, and grace was to be said before and after each meal.
8. There must be "no suspicious talk or contracting matrimony or entering wards of the opposite sex."
9. The sisters must see that no cardplay or dicing took place.
10. The sisters were to clean the wards by 6 a.m. and keep their yards clean and not allow hens in them.
11. No patient was to sit up after 8 p.m. in the winter or 9 p.m. in the summer.
12. Every tenth bed was to be left empty to air and not more than one patient was to be put in each bed.

It is strange that nurses are not mentioned in the minutes until 1701, when three nurses or "helpers" were appointed. There had been an assistant sister in each of the larger wards for nearly thirty years. Some of the sisters and nurses continued to work long after reaching an age now regarded as normal for retirement. In 1708 Sister Lydia was pensioned off at the age of seventy-seven.

By 1712 the number of in-patients had increased to 350, and each month there were eighty out-patients. Apparently the next few years saw a big increase in the latter, for in 1715 it was decided to restrict the number of out-patients to forty a day, and none of them was to visit the hospital more than once a month, unless specially recommended to do so. Both in-patients and out-patients had to produce a letter from a governor or a church-warden before admission. The increase in the number of patients led to a need for more medical staff, and by 1723 there were four surgeons and three physicians.

The surgeons received only £40 a year, but they augmented their salaries by the fees they received from their pupils, who paid twenty-four guineas for twelve months. Although each pupil was supposed to be under the supervision of a particular surgeon, all the fees were collected and divided equally among the surgeons and apothecaries of St. Thomas's and Guy's Hospital. For some time after the latter was founded, there was very close collaboration between the two hospitals. The number of pupils that a surgeon might have at any particular time was restricted: in 1724 it was limited to three, but in 1726 it was increased to four.

CHAPTER IV

THE AGE OF HOSPITALS

THE eighteenth century was a very important one in the history of English hospitals, for it saw the beginning of the great voluntary hospital movement which served this country so well for nearly 250 years. The century has, in fact, been called "The Age of Hospitals." England was now a prosperous nation, with a flourishing trade and agriculture which brought great wealth to a good proportion of her citizens. Some of these thought of little but their wealth and of ways of increasing it for their own advantage, but many of them were struck by the great difference between their riches and the poverty of thousands of their fellow countrymen. Although they had little or none of the great religious zeal which had belonged to their ancestors of the Middle Ages, they felt that they should use some of their wealth to help to alleviate the distress of those less fortunate than themselves. The relief of sickness was an obvious way in which this could be done. Some of them had been abroad and had seen that, compared with England, a number of the continental countries were well-provided with hospitals. In the words of the founders of the Royal Hampshire County Hospital at Winchester, they realised that these hospitals constituted "a charity which is the glory of other countries and has long been the reproach of our own."

It seems to have been the French Huguenot refugees who settled in London after the revocation of the Edict of Nantes in 1685 who set the example by founding the first establishment for the sick poor in the city to be supported entirely by voluntary contributions. In 1708 one of these Huguenots left a sum of money for the erection and maintenance of a hospital for his poorer fellow refugees. The French Protestant Hospital was founded; its rules forbade admission to all except French Protestants or their descendants living in Great Britain. The money which the founder had left proved inadequate, and so an appeal was made for voluntary contributions—an example that was followed by the promoters of other hospitals all over the country.

The first practical step by Englishmen towards making good the deficiency of hospitals was taken in London in 1716, when Henry Hoare, a merchant-banker, William Wogan, a writer on religious subjects, Robert Witham, a brewer, and Patrick Cockburn, a former curate, met at St. Dunstan's Coffee House and discussed the plight of the poor sick people of Westminster. They prepared and published a "Charitable Proposal for Relieving the Sick and Needy, and other Distressed Persons." In this document, which was really an appeal for funds, they expressed the opinion that "Nothing but the Revival of the True Christian Spirit of Justice and Charity in the Persons employ'd to take care of the poor and the voluntary assistance of others acted by the same spirit" could remedy the miserable state of so many of their fellow-citizens.

The "Charitable Proposal" did not actually mention the idea of establishing a hospital. In the preamble it was explained that "a proposal for the more easy and effectual relief of the sick and needy" had been "communicated to some persons who have been engaged in the promoting of several pious and charitable works." These people had held a number of meetings and had resolved "with God's grace and assistance to undertake and carry on the design mentioned in the said proposal and agreed to meet constantly once a week for that purpose." Their aim was the establishment of a charitable society to provide food, medicine, medical advice, nursing care, and visitors to the sick. The people who were to receive these services were to be chiefly the poor of the parish of St. Margaret's, Westminster, although sick foreigners would be assisted to return to their own countries, and visits would be arranged to prisoners who were ill. Those who read the "Charitable Proposal" and could afford to contribute money were asked to do so. Those who could not give cash were requested to "give what they have to spare, as broken victuals, old clothes, linen, beds, bedding, chairs, stools, pots, dishes, glasses, etc." It was not only actual money or goods which were required; active assistance was also needed. "Those of either sex who are freed from the incumbrances and distractions of worldly affairs" could help by visiting, reading, mending and seeking aid from others.

In the first three months of 1716 a number of meetings were held and sick people were helped in various ways. Then, at the beginning of April, it was reported that no more money was available. Meetings continued to take place for another month, but after that well over three years elapsed before there was any further assembly.

In December, 1719, twelve men met at St. Dunstan's Coffee House. Of the original four, only Hoare and Wogan remained. It appears that they had not been idle during the long interval since the last meeting, for it was stated that they had collected money "for the procuring, furnishing, and defraying the necessary expenses of an infirmary or place of entertainment for such poor sick persons inhabiting in the parish of St. Margaret's, Westminster, or others who shall be recommended by any of the subscribers or benefactors with the approbation and consent of the major part of the trustees present." The trustees were all those who subscribed to the charity; this had been decided at one of the meetings in 1716. It was an unwise decision, for the number of subscribers ran into several hundreds. Since the majority of them sometimes attended the meetings and all had the right to speak and vote, these were often lengthy affairs.

Before the end of the year Dr. Alexander Stewart had agreed to be the physician of the infirmary and Mrs. Jane Alden, a widow, had been appointed matron at a salary of £6 a year. But the infirmary did not yet exist, for no suitable building had been found, although an intensive search was being made. There was not sufficient money to purchase a property, so one would have to be rented, and it was this that caused the difficulty, for several people who were approached would not allow their houses to be used as hospitals. At last, however, a building in Petty France was obtained for £22 a year, but even this action met with opposition from a doctor who lived opposite and complained that a hospital would be a nuisance to everybody dwelling near it.

The tenancy commenced on Lady Day, 1720. A month later it was decided to inscribe on the walls of the house in gold letters the words "Infirmary for the sick and needy." The matron and her small staff moved in. They consisted of a nurse who was paid £5 14s. 0d. a year, a maidservant who received £4, and a messenger boy whose annual wage was £3. In addition they had free board and lodging and an allowance of beer. On 11th May the trustees decided that the first patient, John Kelly, should be admitted on the following day. He suffered from "evil in his joints and scurvy," and stayed in the infirmary nearly a month before he was discharged cured.

The minutes of the trustees' meetings held during the next few years are very interesting, for they reveal many details of life in the first voluntary hospital. Mrs. Cam was admitted with asthma and dropsy, but was soon discharged as incurable. The first child patient was an eight-years-old boy who had a carious bone on the lower part of his knee. Dr. Stewart thought a bathing tub would be very useful, so "one of the largest size" was bought for four guineas. In the first two months fifteen in-patients and fifteen out-patients received treatment. Of these, only one died, and she was an old woman of eighty who had St. Anthony's fire (erysypelas). It was decided to follow the practice at St. Bartholomew's and St. Thomas's Hospitals and insist that when a patient was admitted sufficient money must be deposited to meet the cost of his or her burial. No visitors were to stay after 9 p.m. When patients were discharged they had to appear before the Board and give thanks to God and to the trustees for their cure. Then, when they had left the hospital, they had to go to their parish churches and give thanks again in public. Apothecaries were invited to submit tenders for the supply of drugs. During the second year of its existence the total cost of running the hospital was £390 16s. 8d., but there was money in hand, for receipts amounted to £535 11s. 8½d.

Mrs. Alden and her small staff had to care for about a dozen patients at a time. She had to work very hard, for there was no night nurse, and in addition to nursing she had to look after the supplies and supervise the domestic work. In 1723 her salary was raised to £9. She managed to carry out her onerous duties for sixteen years before she retired because of ill-health; then the Board showed their gratitude by presenting her with £5!

The Westminster Hospital did not stay long in Petty France. In 1724 it moved to a bigger house in Caxton Street. This, too, was only occupied for a few years; in 1733 it became apparent that a new home would have to be found without delay, for the building was falling down. There was a dispute over the new site, and this quarrel is of importance because it led to the foundation of another great London hospital.

The vice-president of the Board said he was prepared to let to the Governors some houses belonging to him near Petty France. A committee, whose members included the physicians and surgeons, reported that the buildings were suitable, but before agreement was reached regarding the tenancy Dr. Stewart suggested that a house at Hyde Park Corner might provide better accommodation. The Board disagreed with this, but the medical staff, who only a few weeks before had been in favour of the site near Petty France, now refused to go there, and all of them moved to Hyde Park Corner, where they had obtained a lease of Lanesborough House for £60 a year, and there they founded St. George's Hospital. (In fairness to the medical men concerned, it must be pointed out that they agreed to continue to visit the Westminster Hospital until other physicians and surgeons were appointed there.) The dispute was really a fortunate affair, for now the sick of London had two hospitals instead of only one.

Lanesborough House was a mansion built by the second Viscount Lanesborough in 1719. When it was acquired as a hospital it was still surrounded by open fields. This was one of the reasons which had led to its choice being favoured by the medical men; in their own words it was far enough from the city "for the patients to have the benefit of a country air, which in the general opinion of the physicians would be more effectual than physick in the cure of many distempers."

At first there were only two wards, each with fifteen beds. Six physicians and three surgeons agreed to act as medical officers "without fee or reward." Donations poured in; men who subscribed £5 annually were eligible for election as governors. The man and his wife who had acted as caretakers of Lanesborough House for the Lanesborough family were appointed porter and matron. Other appointments were those of a "secretary and register" and an apothecary, both unpaid. One nurse was engaged for each ward; they were paid £6 a year and provided with board and lodging. The cook's salary was £7 a year.

The first patient was admitted on 1st January 1734, and during that month sixty-four others received treatment. They consisted of ten with consumption (two of whom died), eight with intermittent fever (one death), one with diarrhoea (who died), five with rheumatism (one death), two with chlorosis, three with fractures, eleven with ulcers, two with tumours of the breast, two with caries of the leg, two with glandular tumours, and one with each of the following ailments: jaundice, herpes, albugo, ringworm, rupture, stone in the bladder, scorbutic eruptions, flux, contusion, gravel, worm fever, pain in the breasts, palsy, ophthalmia, fever, asthma, dropsy, spinaventose and colic.

The number of beds had to be rapidly increased; by 1745 there were 250, although often there was insufficient money for all of them to be used. For example, in 1744 only about one hundred were occupied. The cost of a bed was about £30 a year. By October 1734, the staff had grown to a matron, an apothecary, a messenger, seven nurses, a cook, a housemaid and an apothecary's man.

The matron, who was paid £10 a year, had a long list of duties. She had "to take care of all the household goods and furniture, according to the inventory, and account for the same, see that the inferior servants do their duty, and in case of misbehaviour or neglect acquaint the treasurer or visitors; take charge of all the door-keys, and see that the outer doors be always locked

from 9 p.m. to 7 a.m. from Michaelmas to Lady Day, and from
10 p.m. to 5 a.m. from Lady Day to Michaelmas, unless she were
ordered otherwise by the governors or visitors; see that no patient
be allowed out of the house without leave of the physicians,
surgeons or apothecaries, and that leave be not given to any
patient to go into St. James's Park or the Green Park upon any
pretence whatever; see that no gin, or other strong liquors, shall
be brought into the house by or to any patient, and if any such
be found it shall be taken away; keep a daily account of all the
meat, bread and other provisions and necessaries brought into
the house, and how much has been consumed, and that no broken
bread or meat be carried out by any patient or servant; that the
men patients shall not be allowed in the women's ward and vice-
versa; take care that the rooms, clothes and linen of the patients
are kept clean and decent; that there be no playing at cards, dice
or other games in any of the wards, and visit them frequently for
that purpose; report to the weekly board, treasurers or visitors
all misdemeanours or other matters which may prejudice the
charity; and give account every Wednesday morning of the
number of empty beds." In her duty of accounting for provisions
the matron received help from the clerk, who was required to
assist her "to weigh or measure meat, bread, butter, cheese and
all other provisions, and keep an exact account of the same."
This clerk, who was paid, had replaced the unpaid "secretary and
register."

Meanwhile, by 1736 the staff at the Westminster had increased
by 250 per cent, and the salaries, although still low by modern
standards, were considerably higher than those paid sixteen years
earlier. They were as follows: apothecary £20 a year; clerk £16;
matron £12; four day nurses and three night nurses £7 each;
messenger £6 11s. 4d.; porter £6; maid £5 10s. 0d.; and cook
£5. They were all provided with board, lodging, laundry and
beer.

Five years later the porter's wages were increased to £8, but
his duties were carefully defined. His working hours were from
6 a.m. to 1 p.m. and from 2.30 p.m. to 10 p.m. every day. He

had to keep the door locked and when he was not on duty he had to give the key to the matron. He could let the nurses and the domestic staff go in or out only when the matron had given permission. He had to ensure that nobody took provisions away and that no spirits or strong beer were brought into the hospital. In addition, he had to record the times when the apothecary and the house pupil came into or left the hospital.

The clerk was responsible for ensuring that all the books were properly kept. He also had to attend all the committee meetings and prepare the minutes. By 1762 his dignity and his duties had increased considerably—and so had his salary. He was now secretary and receiver and was paid £30 per annum. In addition he received 6d. from every guinea which he collected in subscriptions.

The minute books of this period contain entries about matters both great and small. In 1747 a sink was placed in the yard so that the nurses could "wash their necessaries." In 1764 a contract was made for all the apartments and beds to be disinfested of bugs in three weeks for £20. In the same year an architect was consulted about an operating theatre which was to be constructed at an estimated cost of £100. Five years later a much smaller but quite important building occupied the Board's attention—orders were given that the "men's necessary" was to be emptied more frequently. The only source of illumination was still candlelight, and in 1782 it was decreed that the house surgeon must not be allowed more than two candles each evening.

In dealing with St. George's, we jumped ahead a little in our story, for it was the third—not the second—hospital to be founded in London during the eighteenth century. The second place belongs to Guy's Hospital, which was opened in 1726.

Thomas Guy was a London publisher and bookseller. He was very successful at his trade, and by the time he reached middle age was a comparatively wealthy man. For many years he had desired to help those less fortunate than himself. In 1704 he became a governor of St. Thomas's Hospital. Four years later he paid £1,000 for the erection of three new wards and promised to give the hospital £100 every year for its poor patients. Already rich, he multiplied his wealth many times by investing some of his money in government securities, which a little later rose considerably in value, and also in South Sea stock, which he sold at a great profit before the bursting of the famous Bubble. These investments resulted in a rapid increase in his wealth: in three months in 1720 he sold £54,000 of South Sea stock for over £230,000.

He decided to use this money for the benefit of the incurables of St. Thomas's Hospital. By modern standards many of these so-called incurables were not beyond cure, but Guy had watched with distress as they were discharged from St. Thomas's, still ill and too weak to earn their living. He made up his mind he would build a new hospital for these unfortunates, and in 1721 he obtained a lease of some land near St. Thomas's. Four years later the building, the first in London—if we except St. Bartholomew's —to be specially designed as a hospital, was completed. Unfortunately the man whose generosity had made its construction possible did not live to see it brought into use; Guy had died early in 1724.

In his will, after making a number of bequests to relatives and charity, he bequeathed the residue of his estate to nine governors of St. Thomas's Hospital on trust to finish the building of his own hospital, and "to receive therein four hundred poor persons or upwards, labouring under any distempers or disorders, thought capable of relief by physic or surgery." There were to be sixty governors, including a president and a treasurer. These two officers and twenty-one other men were to form the Court of Committees. Seven members of this Court were to retire each year; their successors were to be appointed by the Court of Governors. It was the former Court which did most of the work of controlling the administration of the hospital; the governors merely ratified its decisions, reserving to themselves only the appointment of certain senior officers—medical and surgical staff, the chaplain and the clerk to the governors. It will be noted that Guy wisely avoided a mistake which had been made at the Westminster

Hospital, and ensured that the governing body of his establishment was comparatively small.

At their second meeting the governors appointed two surgeons and two physicians, each of whom was to be paid £40 a year. The first chaplain was appointed in 1726. It appears that the care of the patients' souls was rated more highly than the care of their bodies, for his annual salary was £80—twice as much as that of a physician or a surgeon. The first matron also received more than the medical officers; her salary was £50, with free coal and small beer. Eleven sisters were appointed; they were paid £25, but were required to give £10 as surety for their honesty.

Compared with the other hospitals founded in the eighteenth century, the staff of Guy's were more numerous and for the most part better paid; it must be remembered, however, that it was larger than the other hospitals. The total annual bill for salaries and wages was over £1,300, and the staff, in addition to the officers mentioned above, included a treasurer, who held the same office at St. Thomas's Hospital and received his salary there; a clerk, who was paid £40 a year; a steward (£80); an apothecary (£80); a butler (£67 2s. 8d.); eight nurses (£16 each); and twelve watchwomen (£10 8s. 0d. each).

The hospital was opened and patients were admitted in January 1726. At first there were sixty, but this number was soon increased to one hundred.

The regulations laid down by the governors included measures against swearing, smoking and gambling. A patient found smoking or gambling was discharged. The rules regarding swearing were not quite so harsh: the user of bad language was not discharged until his third offence. On the first occasion he was heard swearing he would be deprived of food for one day, and on the second occasion he would get no food for two days.

Towards the end of the century various improvements were made at the hospital. In 1780 cold, hot and vapour baths were installed. In 1799 Guy's became the first hospital in London to appoint a dental surgeon. Throughout its early years Guy's, like the other hospitals of the time, experienced infestations of bugs.

In 1735 a man was paid £20 for killing the bugs and sixty years later we find that the bug-catcher had become a permanent member of the staff and was receiving a salary equal to that of a physician or a surgeon.

Another great hospital founded in the metropolis during the first half of the eighteenth century was the London Hospital. Seven men met at the Feather's Tavern, Cheapside, on 23rd September 1740, and one of them, Mr. Harrison, "delivered in the lease of the house taken for the intended Infirmary, which was approved." They agreed that "with the sum already sub-scribed [100 guineas]" it was "proper to begin the said Charity." From the wording of these minutes it appears that there had been previous meetings. The house chosen was in Featherstone Street and the rent was £16 per annum.

The seven men lost no time in opening their hospital. A week later they held another meeting and engaged a man and woman to look after the house; their joint annual salary was £20. Two of the founders were authorised to purchase furniture at a cost not exceeding £15. Another week passed and then the treasurer, surgeon, physician and apothecary were appointed. The surgeon, John Harrison, who was one of the seven founders, was only twenty-two years old. It was decided to open the hospital in November, but only a fortnight before the appointed day the treasurer reported that "there be only one shilling in the Bank!" Despite this serious state of affairs, the men decided to go ahead with their plans. It might have been expected that they would ask their treasurer to advise them on the action to be taken to get them out of their financial difficulties; instead, they requested their young surgeon to consider what should be done and submit a report at the next meeting. When this took place, Harrison was able to tell them that he had managed to raise ten guineas and also persuade the Duke of Richmond to become an annual sub-scriber. The founders felt that ten guineas was a sufficient balance, and on 3rd November the London Infirmary, as it was then called, was opened.

It was a hospital without nurses; all the work had to be done by the man and woman, the sole full-time members of the staff. The physician, surgeon and apothecary visited the hospital daily from 8 a.m. to 10 a.m. in the summer and 9 a.m. to 11 a.m. in the winter. In addition, the apothecary attended on one afternoon a week "for the practice of midwifery and the distempers incident thereto." Unfortunately the number of patients is not known, but it was probably quite small.

All those who subscribed five guineas to the funds of the infirmary were entitled to be known as managers or governors and to attend meetings which were held in a tavern on alternate Tuesday evenings. The subscribers appointed a committee to deal with the day-to-day management of the hospital; this committee met at the infirmary every Thursday morning. The meetings were summoned for 10 a.m., but business did not commence until 11 a.m. Any member who was not there by that time had to put a shilling in the poor-box. Apparently the meetings were lengthy affairs, for one of the minutes is as follows: "Resolved that this Committee for the future do adjourn to the Angel and Crown Tavern, Whitechapel, at 4 o'clock, for the better transacting the business of the Infirmary." Two members of the House Committee were appointed to act as House Visitors for fortnightly periods.

Although, when the hospital opened, the only full-time members of the staff were one man and one woman, this situation could not, of course, continue for long, and nurses had to be engaged. The committee drew up standing orders regarding their duties. They had to commence work at 6 a.m. and continue until supper time at 10 p.m. They had to be in bed within one hour of going off duty. Their work included making the beds of all the staff and cleaning the whole of the hospital. The general attitude towards nurses at that time is clearly shown by one doctor who wrote: "We always engage them without a character, as no respectable person would undertake so disagreeable an office."

Early in 1741 the first secretary was engaged. He was paid ten guineas a year, and his duties were clearly defined—

To reside near the Infirmary; to write all letters to noblemen and others; to attend all courts and committees; to attend the House Visitors twice a week from 11 to 1; and not to be absent without leave from the Chairman; to collect subscriptions; to keep a register of patients' names; to keep the accounts; to make out all summons; and to perform all other work usually performed by secretaries.

The committee do not appear to have been satisfied with his work, particularly the way in which he recorded their deliberations, for they instructed him to write up his minutes immediately after each meeting "before he left the room." However, when he applied for an increase in his salary it was raised, first to £25 and then to £40, although for this addition to his income he was expected to carry out all the legal work of the infirmary. He was not satisfied with this, and embezzled £400 from the infirmary funds. The governors treated him very leniently—far too generously, one would think. Nine of them guaranteed to refund the £400, and they all decided unanimously that he should continue as secretary! It is only fair to him to state that he insisted on resigning.

The infirmary stayed in its first home only a very short time. The house in Featherstone Street was soon found to be too small, and in May 1741, a move was made to a larger building in Prescott Street.

The governors decided to hold a "Court" quarterly to elect twelve of their number to form a House Committee, which would meet weekly. Unlike many modern hospital authorities, this House Committee did not favour the appointment of sub-committees; it wanted to keep the control of all the affairs of the infirmary in its own hands, and this view was clearly set out in the minutes—

It is the opinion of this Committee that the weekly Board of this Infirmary is capable of transacting all the current business of auditing accounts, admitting and dismissing patients, and doing all the business usually done by committees in other hospitals, without appointing any other Committees or any part of the same.

Normally patients were admitted by the Committee only once a week. If an admission was considered necessary between the meetings of the Committee, it had to be authorised by the treasurer or the chairman.

Two nurses—a day nurse and a night nurse—were appointed. The day nurse, who was always referred to by her surname as "Squire," was paid 5s. a week and was non-resident; the night nurse received 3s. 6d. a week. Squire's behaviour, like that of many other nurses of the time, was of a low standard, as the following amazing minute shows—

> Squire was reported to have taken money from the patients; she was not dismissed, however, as it was not in the rules that she should not do so. She promised not to do so again.

The first matron was appointed in 1742 at a salary of £15 per annum. She was allowed sixpence a day for each patient, and had to provide their food out of this sum. She gave them little more than the bare minimum necessary to keep them alive, and nearly all the money went into her own pocket.

In the following year the nurses became resident, and consequently their wages were changed. The salary of a day nurse was £6 per annum; a watch, or night nurse, received £4. The nurses had nowhere to entertain their friends, so they received them in the room where the watches slept, which, of course, disturbed the watches. When the House Visitors reported this to the Committee it was decided that the nurses must receive their visitors in the kitchen!

A number of students were accepted at the infirmary for instruction in surgery. This was chiefly due to the zeal of Mr. Harrison and his popularity as a teacher. Each pupil was accepted for one year. Some of Harrison's ideas were well in advance of his time. For example, he asked the Committee to remove all the paper from the walls of the wards and have them varnished, so that they could be washed down.

From as early as 1741 the infirmary had a chaplain. He was a local clergyman who volunteered to do this work, for which he received no payment. He read prayers twice a week, and also preached a sermon once a fortnight; this was attended by the Committee.

During the first year of its existence, 127 in-patients received treatment in the infirmary; of these, ten died. The total expenditure was £206 5s. 6d. By far the most costly item was drugs and dressings, which accounted for £63 3s. 1d. Salaries and wages cost £27 15s. 5d., provisions £27 11s. 6d., and stationery £9 15s. 11d., but only 10s. 6d. was spent on soap! Income exceeded expenditure by more than ninety pounds.

A patient could receive treatment only if he was recommended by a subscriber. This led to difficulties, for the list of subscribers was large, and they were widely scattered: they included every bishop in England. Often a subscriber sent a person to the infirmary without first making sure that a bed was vacant. When this happened, the person concerned was treated as an out-patient until a bed became available. The pressure was so great that in 1742 an additional house was acquired. Each patient had to pay a shilling "for the use of utensils"; this was the only payment demanded. After patients had been cured they were required to go to the chapel and acknowledge the benefits they had received, and also appear before the next meeting of the Committee and express their thanks. If they failed to do this, they were refused any treatment in the future. Convalescent patients were allowed to leave the hospital during the daytime; if they did not return in the evening they were never admitted again.

The dietary was very poor: "milk pottige" or water gruel for breakfast, boiled meat or a boiled or baked pudding for dinner, and broth or "milk pottige" for supper. If a patient did not like these dishes, he had to go without; even if, because of his illness, they were quite unsuitable for him, no alternatives were provided, for, according to the minutes, "it was agreed that no other diet be expected or allowed on any account whatever."

Two interesting changes were made in the governing body. Ladies who subscribed five guineas were made governors and were allowed to vote by proxy. The same voting privilege was extended to all peers.

By 1745 further accommodation was necessary, and three more houses were leased. "A shed at the bottom of the garden" was provided as a waiting-room for out-patients; previously, whatever the weather, they had to wait out of doors until their turn for treatment arrived. A cold bath was also installed. There was only one pair of sheets for each bed, so that patients frequently had to use sheets in which previous patients had died.

Within a couple of years it became obvious that the infirmary could not remain long in its five houses. They were not large enough and they were in a bad state of repair. The Bishop of Worcester launched an appeal for funds at the infirmary's annual festival. This ceremony had been instituted in 1742. A bishop preached a sermon at one of the nearby churches, and then all the congregation marched through the streets to the hall of one of the livery companies, where they had dinner. Those who partook of the meal had to buy tickets, and the entire proceeds of these went to the infirmary's funds, since the cost of the banquet was met by those governors who were appointed festival stewards for the year. The Bishop's appeal was very successful; within twelve months £5,000 had been received, and the search for a site for the new building began. After lengthy negotiations some land in Whitechapel Road was leased from the City Council. The erection of a hospital to accommodate 350 patients was commenced in 1752, but because of delays in obtaining funds it was not completed until 1759, although the first patients were admitted two years earlier.

The accounts for 1767 show that the cost per bed per annum was £17 15s. od. An important step towards getting rid of bugs was taken in 1772, when iron bedsteads were first used; most of the other hospitals continued to use wooden bedsteads for many years. However, the London was not quite as advanced in other respects, for in 1789 a House Visitor reported "that there are no towels allowed in any of the women's wards, nor soap for the hands, etc., of any of the patients."

In 1782 the surgeons asked if a theatre could be built where lectures could be given. Their request was granted, but they were required to meet the cost of erection. In the following year the hospital's medical school was founded. Previously, when a surgeon or physician acquired an apprentice he had to take the young man to a meeting of the House Committee, introduce him, and ask the Committee's permission for him to "walk" the hospital in order to gain experience. At first the apprentices had to "walk" the wards for a year, but later, as the number of apprentices increased, the time was reduced to six months. When they were not "walking" the hospital the students had plenty of time and opportunity to get into mischief. It was a common practice for them to invite their friends into the hospital and show them around, and if one of these friends happened to be the worse for drink he would often be allowed to sleep in one of the beds in a ward.

CHAPTER V

THE AGE OF HOSPITALS
(continued)

ANOTHER great London hospital founded about the same time as the London was the Middlesex. In 1745 a group of philanthropic citizens rented Nos. 8–10, Windmill Street, for £30 a year, and there opened a fifteen-bedded hospital for the poor of Soho. Within a year the new hospital's finances were in a parlous state and its administration was chaotic. Fortunately it was saved by drastic action on the part of the twenty governors. Three of them, with the treasurer and the physician, were directed to visit "the nobility and others for their subscriptions." Anybody who subscribed three guineas annually or made a single payment of twenty-one guineas became a governor and was allowed to take part in the management of the hospital. These steps soon led to a great improvement in the financial position.

Measures were also taken to end the chaotic state of the administration. A new physician, three new surgeons and an assistant surgeon were appointed. Abraham Foisseau was to be messenger and doorkeeper, his wife was made matron, and one nurse was engaged. The matron had to maintain an inventory of "goods, linen, utensils, etc." A room was set aside for the medical staff, and the apothecary was provided with a dispensary. A steward or superintendent was appointed at a salary of ten guineas a year; he was also provided with "a small press bed" in the committee room. The governors seem to have been unfortunate in their choice of staff, for they soon found it necessary to dismiss the messenger, the matron and the apothecary; according to the minutes, the misdemeanours which brought about the apothecary's downfall were "vile and enormous."

A step taken in 1747 was of importance in the history of English hospitals. It was decided to reserve five beds for lying-in cases. The Middlesex thus became the first lying-in hospital in the country. Soon the number of maternity beds was increased, first to ten and then to twelve (by this time the hospital could accommodate a total of twenty-four patients). But twelve maternity beds proved quite insufficient for populous Soho. So great was the demand that it was decided that the only way to deal with the matter was to open a new hospital. In 1754 the present site in St. Marylebone was leased, an architect agreed to design, build and furnish a hospital for £2,250, and an appeal was launched for funds. One attempt to increase the finances was unusual; it was also, unfortunately, not nearly as successful as had been anticipated. A gentleman aged seventy-four promised to bequeath £600 to the hospital provided it supplied him with everything he required for the rest of his life. When the governors entered into this agreement they obviously had no idea that the old gentleman would live to be eighty-two! Fortunately their other money-making efforts were more successful, and in 1757 a new hospital was opened with sixty-four beds and including a separate maternity department.

All the hospitals mentioned so far were general hospitals; the great development of the specialist hospitals did not come until the nineteenth century, although a few of them were established in the eighteenth century. The necessity for them was realised because the so-called general hospitals were not really general hospitals. Most of them refused to treat certain ailments; the Westminster, for example, would not admit incurables, lunatics, lying-in women, and sufferers from V.D. and such infectious diseases as smallpox. Most of the early hospitals were also specialist in another sense: admission was usually restricted to patients living in a certain area. The first hospital for patients from all over the country was the Bath General Hospital, which was founded in 1738 for the purpose of making available to everybody the curative properties of the waters of the spa.

Two specialist hospitals were founded in 1746. One was the Middlesex County Hospital for smallpox and inoculation. The other was the London Lock Hospital for venereal diseases. Its founders, Martin Madan, a clergyman, and William Bromfield, a surgeon, had to struggle against the popular prejudices of the time. The other hospitals would not admit syphilitic patients because the disease was regarded as a just punishment for the sins of the sufferers. The London Lock Hospital was opened in a building near Hyde Park Corner early in 1747. It had thirty beds. In less than three years nearly seven hundred patients were admitted and over 640 of these were discharged cured.

A few years earlier, in 1739, the country's leading obstetrician, Sir Richard Manningham, had opened a house in London as a lying-in hospital. Seventy years later, after it had changed its address several times, this was to become the famous Queen Charlotte's Lying-In Hospital. It led the way in the fight against two more prejudices: it was the first lying-in hospital to admit unmarried women and it was also the first to admit male resident students.

Another step towards specialisation was taken at the Middlesex in 1792, when a ward was set aside for cancer patients. The hospital was able to do this, despite financial difficulties, because of a gift of £3,000 from Samuel Whitbread, the brewer.

While new hospitals were springing up all over the country, the two old stalwarts, St. Bartholomew's and St. Thomas's, continued to flourish. The second half of the century saw a number of improvements at St. Thomas's, where, it is interesting to note, the cost of the patients admitted during the six years between 1751 and 1757 was 16s. 11½d. each.

In 1761 the following diet scale was authorised—

Full Diet

Breakfast Milk porridge on four days a week and water gruel on three days.

Dinner ½ lb. meat on five days and 4 oz. butter or 6 oz. cheese on two days.

Supper 1 pint broth.

Bread 14 oz. a day.

Beer 1 quart in winter and 3 pints in summer.

Middle or Low Diet

Breakfast As for full diet.
Dinner 6 oz. mutton or veal on five days a week, and 4 oz. butter or 6 oz. cheese on two days.
Supper Milk porridge on four days and water gruel on three days.
Bread 12 oz. a day.
Beer 1 quart.

Milk Diet

Breakfast As for full diet.
Dinner 1 pint rice milk on four days a week and 8 oz. pudding on three days.
Supper As for middle diet.
Milk and
water 1 quart ($\frac{1}{3}$ milk) in winter, 3 pints in summer.
Bread 12 oz. daily.

Dry Diet

Breakfast 2 oz. cheese or butter.
Dinner As for full diet.
Supper As for breakfast.
Bread 14 oz., or 5 sea biscuits, daily.
Beer 1 quart daily.

Fever Diet

Barley water, water gruel, panado (a mixture of butter, flour and milk), thin broth, milk porridge, rice gruel, and sage tea.

Three years later, in 1764, the first step was taken towards ridding the hospital of the bugs with which, like all hospitals of the time, it was infested. Several of the governors subscribed five guineas each in order to provide iron bedsteads for one ward, in place of the old wooden ones. As a result, this ward was freed from bugs, and three years later an appeal was made for money for iron bedsteads throughout the remainder of the hospital.

Rising costs made it impossible to continue to admit patients without payment. In 1769 it was decided that "clean" patients should pay 2s. 6d. on admission and "foul" patients (i.e. those suffering from venereal diseases) 17s. 6d.

In 1792 the governors felt that there should be some special inducement to encourage the nursing staff in their work. They therefore decided to award six prizes of four guineas each to the three sisters and three nurses in the clean wards who best satisfied the staff.

Although by modern standards the London hospitals of the late eighteenth century left much to be desired, particularly in the way of cleanliness, they were, apparently, superior to many hospitals on the Continent. In 1788 a French tourist commented on their orderliness, method and cleanliness, three qualities which were completely lacking in French hospitals. The French nurses, however, exhibited far more tenderness and devotion towards the sick than did their English counterparts. This the tourist ascribed to the fact that the nurses in French hospitals were mostly Sisters of Mercy, who were inspired by their religion and did not nurse merely for the sake of earning their living.

If the French tourist visited Westminster Hospital he may have been shocked to find that religious discrimination was practised there. In 1741 a rule was made that no Roman Catholic patient should be admitted unless he first made known his religion; if a person failed to do this and was later discovered to be a Catholic, he had to be discharged immediately. Later this discrimination was applied also to the staff, and the employment of Roman Catholics was forbidden. Possibly these regulations were repealed before the arrival of the French tourist, for it is known that during the French Revolution refugee priests were admitted.

The governors of the Westminster tried to provide something in the nature of a library. They ordered that copies of the following books should be placed on the prayer desk in each ward, in addition to the Bible and the Prayer Book: *The Whole Duty of Man*; *Death* and *Judgment*, both by Sherlock; *Death* by Kettlewell; *Thomas à Kempis* by Stanhope; Kettlewell's *Companion for*

Penitents; St. Augustine's *Meditations*; and *The Sick Man Visited* by Spink. There is no record of the number of patients who read these books—or whether anybody read them at all!

At most hospitals during the eighteenth century there was keen competition whenever the post of a surgeon or physician became vacant. The election of a successor was carried out by the whole Board of Governors, and this was the one occasion when they turned up in force. It was not unusual for several hundred of them to crowd into the board room when an election was to take place. A retiring surgeon's word carried much influence in the appointment of his successor and this led to bribery, for a doctor who wanted to obtain a hospital appointment would often pay a large sum to a surgeon on the understanding that the latter would nominate him as his successor.

The surgeons had apprentices, known as "cubs." At the Westminster each surgeon was allowed to have three cubs, while the apothecary was permitted to have one resident pupil.

At Guy's the rules were not quite as strict. The surgeons there were each allowed to have four pupils and four dressers at a time, inclusive of apprentices. A dresser did not have quite as many privileges as an apprentice, but he was permitted to assist at operations. The fees which an apprentice had to pay were very high: they might be as much as 500 guineas for a full course. A dresser paid £50 a year and a pupil 24 guineas. These fees were shared between the surgeons and the apothecaries of Guy's and St. Thomas's. The two hospitals worked closely together in so far as the instruction of future doctors was concerned; they had an arrangement whereby the older hospital concentrated on surgical teaching while all the medical teaching was given at Guy's.

The governors of the Middlesex Hospital drew up a code of rules of conduct for the pupils. They had to attend "at the dressing of the patients and carry pen, ink and paper to minute down all messages to the physicians." They must not "reduce any fracture or perform any operation of consequence," enter the apothecary's shop, or go into the women's wards except when the patients were being dressed. They were ordered to report "any incident of swearing or other misbehaviour to the first surgeon who next comes to the Hospital."

The surgeons at the Middlesex had been allowed to have pupils since 1746, but physician-pupils were not permitted until twenty years later. At first they did very little except walk around the wards with the physicians, but it was soon realised that the instruction they received in this way was far from sufficient, so the Board decided that the physicians and surgeons should be allowed to give lectures.

Within a few years after the first physician-pupils were allowed, there were enough students to form a Medical Society. The society paid three guineas a quarter for the privilege of meeting in the physicians' room on two nights each week. A condition attached to this rental was that the society must provide its own candles.

The elections held to appoint new physicians and surgeons have been mentioned. A similar procedure was adopted to fill vacancies amongst other senior staff. In 1767 the following advertisement was published in several newspapers by the governors of the London Hospital—

> An Extraordinary General Court of Governors of this Charity will be held on Wednesday, the 30th instant, for the election of Secretary to succeed Mr. William Trotter, deceased. Which election will be carried on by ballot, to begin at 10 o'clock in the forenoon and close at 2 o'clock in the afternoon. And the candidates for the said office are to deliver their petitions to the House Committee in their own handwritings on Tuesday, the 22nd instant before 12 o'clock, as none will be received after that time.

Towards the end of the century, during the wars with France, a number of hospitals found themselves in financial difficulties. At the Middlesex things became so bad that linseed meal had to be used instead of bread for making poultices, and the staff's rations were reduced to $\frac{1}{2}$ lb. butter, 1 lb. cheese and one quartern loaf weekly. This led to the threat of a strike, but fortunately the authorities managed to avert this by adding a small quantity of rice to the rations.

The finances of the Middlesex were helped a little by the admission of the first paying patients. They were French exiles, who paid "eight shillings a week, exclusive of burial fees, nurses' wages and bedding." Some hospitals also obtained money by means of musical performances in Westminster Abbey.

The governors of St. George's made the following orders—

> The board taking into account the enormous increase of expense in all the necessaries of life resolve to observe the utmost economy. Owing to the exigencies of the present time no wheat or flour are to be brought into the hospital till further orders. All the patients are to be allowed boiled rice and no bread on those days when they have meat, unless particularly ordered otherwise by the physician or surgeon. Nurses and servants are allowed daily half a pound of bread with an addition of rice. Two days a week two white or corned herrings instead of meat and one pound of potatoes.

The surgeons were asked to "make trial of poultices without oil, and abolish butter and cheese for the patients, giving instead one pint of milk porridge or gruel."

The provinces did not linger long behind the capital in establishing voluntary hospitals; in fact, they almost preceded it. As early as 1719 John Addenbrooke, a Cambridge physician, bequeathed his fortune for the erection of a small hospital for the university town, although it was not until 1766 that the hospital was actually opened. The first hospital in the provinces was the County Hospital at Winchester, which was opened in 1736. It was closely followed by the Bristol Royal Infirmary.

Towards the end of 1736 the following declaration, inscribed in a vellum book, was signed by seventy-eight citizens of Bristol—

> Whereas many sick persons languish and die miserably for want of necessaries who are not entitled to parochial relief, and whereas amongst them who do receive parochial relief, many suffer extremely, and are sometimes lost partly for want of accommodation and proper medicines in their own houses and lodgings (the closeness or unwholesomeness of which is sometimes one great cause of their sickness) partly by imprudent laying out what is allowed, and by the ignorance or ill-management of those about them—we whose names are underwritten (in obedience to the rules of our holy

Religion) desiring as far as in us lies to find some remedy for this great misery of our poor neighbours—do subscribe the following sums of money, to be by us continued yearly during pleasure, for the procuring, furnishing, and defraying the necessary expence of An Infirmary at Bristol for the benefit of the poor sick, who shall be recommended by any of the Subscribers or Benefactors in such manner as the majority of them shall direct.

The sums promised by the seventy-eight signatories ranged from two guineas to six guineas, and it was decided that everybody who contributed two guineas or more annually should be a trustee as long as he kept up his payments. A person making one contribution of twenty guineas would be a trustee for life. The trustees wasted little time, for they met on 7th January and resolved "That no Physician, Surgeon, Treasurer or Secretary to be employed by this Society shall receive any Salary, Reward or Gratuity from the Society or any Person whatsoever for his Trouble or attendance." Six months later they obtained a lease of some buildings and appointed four physicians, two surgeons and an apothecary. The apothecary was not included in the resolution, and so he was paid a salary of £30 per annum, while his assistant received £5. The matron's salary was only half that of the apothecary, but she also had an annual gratuity of five guineas. Despite the meagre financial reward, she remained at her post until she died thirty-three years later.

In December 1737, the infirmary was opened with thirty-four patients—seventeen of each sex. They had wooden bedsteads, which were placed close together. They were expected to provide their own linen, but those who were unable to do so were supplied with nightdresses and nightcaps. Those who were capable of doing any work had to help in the wards and also make bandages. They were allowed to go for walks on weekdays and to church on Sundays, but they were forbidden to smoke, to swear, or to play cards or dice. A notice in the wards instructed them: "That no Patients do lie in a Bed with their Cloathes on—nor on the Bed with their Shoes." The privilege of going to church was soon withdrawn, because it was reported of some of the patients that "on their return they but too clearly exhibited marks of having been to the alehouse instead of the church."

The wards were very bare, without pictures or any decorations. There was one table bearing a basin and an ewer and various bandages and ointments. When the surgeon came on his rounds he wore no white coat, but only his ordinary clothing, including his hat. His remedy for most ailments was bleeding; on most days the number of people bled was thirty or more, and it is recorded that in seven months one surgeon took forty-seven gallons of blood.

One of the rooms was allocated for the bleeding of out-patients. They sat on a bench and the apothecary tied bandages round their arms and then opened a vein in each person. The patient was given a basin to catch his blood in. Of course, the blood was often spilt, and so the carpet on the floor was red, in order that the stains should not be too obvious.

Far more unpleasant were the operations, which were per-formed on an ordinary wooden table without anaesthetics and with only brandy or laudanum to deaden the pain. If a finger had to be amputated, then the unfortunate patient had to place his hand on a block of wood while the operation was carried out with a hammer and a chisel.

The physicians' methods were as antiquated as those of the surgeons. For example, they tried to cure stone in the bladder with a medicine made from "snails burnt to blackness, chamomile flowers, sweet fennel and greater burdock."

Fifteen of the trustees, known as House Visitors, had to carry out an inspection of the infirmary twice weekly. During the visit they had to see all persons seeking admission as patients and decide which of them should be allowed to receive treatment. The visitors kept a careful watch on the provisions; one of the first entries in their book was "Examined the beer and find it not good enough for the price." The importance attached to value for money as far as this beverage was concerned can be under-stood when it is realised that more was spent on beer than on any other item of provisions. The amount paid for beer in a year was nearly four times the sum spent on milk. This high expenditure worried the Board and in an effort to reduce their costs they bought three houses and converted them into a brewery and a bakehouse. Apparently some members were not satisfied with the watch which the visitors kept on the quality of the foodstuffs, for the matron was instructed to place a loaf of bread, some cheese and a jug of beer on the Board Room table at every meeting.

Other voluntary hospitals established in the provinces during the eighteenth century included—

1743 Devon and Exeter Hospital.
1745 Gloucester Infirmary.
1745 Shrewsbury Infirmary.
1745 Liverpool Royal Infirmary.
1746 Worcester Royal Infirmary.
1752 Manchester Royal Infirmary.
1767 Leeds Infirmary.
1769 Lincoln County Hospital.
1770 Radcliffe Infirmary, Oxford.
1771 Leicester Infirmary.
1776 Hereford General Infirmary.
1782 Nottingham General Hospital.
1783 Kent Dispensary and Miller Hospital.
1784 Hull Royal Infirmary.
1787 Wakefield Hospital.

The early history of most of these establishments and the conditions which existed in them were rather similar to those at Bristol. The following points from their histories give a little fuller idea of English hospitals in the eighteenth century—

1742 The wooden beds at the Bristol Royal Infirmary were replaced by iron bedsteads, and curtains were hung around them. A rather crude contraption consisting of a piece of rope and a cross handle of wood was hung over each bed to enable the patient to raise himself up.

1747 The secretary of Worcester Royal Infirmary, who was paid ten guineas a year, hired a horse and travelled to various places in Worcestershire in an effort to enlist new subscribers.

1752 The Board of the Manchester Royal Infirmary decided "that no person who is supposed to have the venereal disease be admitted into the Infirmary as an in-patient on any account whatsoever." (Six years later they took a more lenient view and decided that "venereal patients who have contracted the distemper innocently" could be admitted.)

1771 The following entry was made in the minute book of the Manchester Royal Infirmary—

"Ordered that the following directions be given to the nurses:

1. That every patient has clean sheets upon their first admission.
2. That they have clean sheets at least once in three weeks.
3. That two patients be not suffered to be in the same bed except that there is no spare bed in the house.
4. That the patients be not suffered to apply poultices without the presence of the nurse."

1778 The matron of the Worcester Royal Infirmary resigned when she was ordered to sleep in the hospital instead of living out.

1794 The physicians at the Worcester Royal Infirmary complained that the surgeons were treating medical cases, so the committee tried to classify the various types of patients. They were in such a quandary over mixed cases, however, that they decided that their treatment must "be left to the candour of the faculty to decide."

1798 The committee of the Worcester Royal Infirmary published in the local papers the names of those persons who had not paid their subscriptions for two years or more.

They also drew up rules for the apothecary. He was to visit each ward daily and report on the state of the patients to the physicians and surgeons. He must not allow the doctors or anybody else to look at the case notes without leave. He had to obtain permission before sleeping out, and on other occasions when he went out he had to tell the matron and porter where he could be found, and he also had to return before 11 p.m.

The governing authorities of many hospitals in the eighteenth century were troubled by the manner in which the surgeons obtained bodies for the practice of anatomy. When the United Company of Barbers and Surgeons was established by Act of Parliament in the reign of Henry VIII it was granted the exclusive right to conduct anatomical demonstrations. It maintained this monopoly for nearly two hundred years, but as they were allowed to use only the bodies of certain executed criminals the number of medical men who could witness demonstrations was very small. During the eighteenth century medical schools were established in connection with St. Thomas's and St. Bartholomew's Hospitals and in addition a number of private schools were set up. These schools broke the monopoly of the United Company. This meant that more bodies were needed for anatomy demonstrations, but there was no legal method of obtaining them; public opinion was still against the idea of bodies being dissected and this view was so strong that governments were afraid to bring in legislation which would advance the science of surgery. The result was that bodies were obtained by illegal means.

A number of unscrupulous characters carried on a spare-time trade in corpses. Known as body-snatchers, resurrectionists, or sack-'em-up men, they operated at night, robbing graves of corpses, which they sold to surgeons and to medical schools. In 1776 more than a hundred bodies, deposited there by resurrectionists, were found in a shed in Tottenham Court Road. In 1828 a body-snatcher, giving evidence before a Select Committee of the House of Commons, said he had belonged to a gang of half a dozen men who had disposed of 312 bodies during one winter. The average price paid for these bodies was four guineas each.

Some hospital authorities cast a blind eye on the activities of the resurrectionists, yet when their own surgeons had bodies of deceased patients taken to their private houses for dissection they felt they had to take some action. In 1756 the Committee of the London Hospital "being informed that dead Bodys have been carried out of this Hospital contrary to the rules and orders of the Charity; they proceeded to inquire into the Truth of the said information, and having examined John Conchee and John Smith, the Two Beadles, they acknowledged that on Friday night the 8th instant, they had carried out the Body of a Woman in a Hamper by order of Mr. Grindall, and by him desired to leave it at the House of Mr. Douglas, a Surgeon in Mile's Lane, Cannon Street . . . They confessed that they had carried or sent to the Surgeons within these nine months past Four Bodys." When the surgeons were called before the Committee they admitted that this was true, but said they did not know that it was against the rules of the Charity. They were reprimanded and told that it must not happen again, and the beadles were warned that if there were any repetition of the incident they would be punished. Another case of the theft of a body is recorded in the minutes of the Board of Governors of the Bristol Royal Infirmary. In 1769 they had to take action against "the whole body of students for removing a corpse from the coffin and substituting for burial a quantity of sand and wool."

Even the outcry over the notorious case of Burke and Hare was not sufficient to make the government legalise dissection and thus end the trade of the resurrection men. Burke and Hare were two Scotsmen who supplied bodies to the medical schools of Edinburgh—not by digging them up but by murdering a number of unfortunate people. It was not until they had committed sixteen murders that their crimes came to light. Three years later, in 1831, there was a similar case in London. Three men, named Bishop, May and Williams, sold the body of a boy to a porter at King's College. The porter had reason to suspect foul play, and he confided his suspicions to the demonstrator of anatomy, who examined the body and was able to confirm that the boy had been murdered. He managed to delay the departure of the men while he was carrying out the examination, and immediately sent for the police, who took them into custody. They were later tried and two of them were executed.

Six months before the crimes of Burke and Hare were discovered the government had given way to public opinion to the extent of appointing a Select Committee to inquire into the manner in which anatomy was studied and to recommend the best method of making bodies available for dissection. Progress was slow, but the London murder stirred Parliament to action, and the Anatomy Act was passed in 1832. This provided for executors or other persons having legal possession of bodies to allow them to be used for anatomical examination, unless the dead persons had expressed a wish to the contrary, or their relatives objected. In this way the sordid trade of the resurrection men was brought to an end.

CHAPTER VI

THE AGE OF SPECIALISATION

THE founders of the eighteenth-century hospitals had not sufficient knowledge of medicine and surgery to think of specialisation—setting aside certain hospitals for the treatment of particular types of disease. With very few exceptions all their foundations had been general hospitals—general in the sense that they dealt with all types of diseases. There were, however, a very small number of specialist hospitals. Queen Charlotte's Lying-In Hospital had been founded in 1739, the City of London Maternity Hospital in 1750, and the General Lying-In Hospital in 1765. The London Lock Hospital for the treatment of venereal disease was established in 1746. The same year saw the opening of the Middlesex County Hospital for smallpox and inoculation. Fifty years later the craze for sea-bathing led to the establishment of the Sea-Bathing Infirmary at Margate, the country's first hospital for tuberculosis. The man really responsible for founding the infirmary was John Coakley Lettsom, a London physician. Besides believing that cures could be effected by sea-water, he was also an advocate of treatment by fresh air and sunlight. The infirmary was designed by a clergyman who was also an amateur architect, and he was responsible for a remarkable innovation: verandahs were provided where the patients could sleep. The hospital was intended for poor London people suffering from tuberculosis. For sentimental reasons it is still known as the Royal Sea-Bathing Hospital, although sea-bathing now plays very little part in the treatment given there.

By the commencement of the nineteenth century the limitations of the general hospitals were beginning to be more widely realised, and increasing medical knowledge made the need for specialisation apparent. However, like many other similar steps forward in the path of progress, the specialist hospitals met with opposition. They were attacked by those who administered the general hospitals, by some members of the medical profession, and by a few people who alleged that they were founded solely for the benefit of the doctors. Gradually, however, their value was realised: they played an important part not only in giving better treatment but also in improving medical education, for they provided clinical material for specialist studies. The general hospital authorities themselves began to set up special departments.

The specialist hospitals founded during the nineteenth century included the following—

1802   London Fever Hospital.
1805   Moorfields Eye Hospital.
1806   Exeter Eye Hospital.
1814   Royal Hospital for Diseases of the Chest, London.
1816   Royal Ear Hospital, Royal Westminster Ophthalmic Hospital, and the Royal Waterloo Hospital for Children and Women.
1829   Hospital for Children, Manchester.
1835   St. Mark's Hospital for Cancer.
1838   Royal National Orthopaedic Hospital, London, and Metropolitan Ear, Nose and Throat Hospital.
1840   Kensington Children's Hospital.
1847   Samaritan Free Hospital for Women.
1848   Victoria Park Hospital for Diseases of the Heart and Lungs.
1849   London Homoeopathic Hospital.
1850   London Smallpox Hospital.
1851   Free Cancer Hospital, Fulham.
1852   Hospital for Sick Children, Great Ormond Street, London.
1854   Royal Hospital for Incurables, Putney.
1855   Poplar Hospital for Accidents.
1857   National Hospital for Diseases of the Heart, the Royal Eye Hospital and the Liverpool Infirmary for Children.
1858   Royal Dental Hospital.
1859   National Hospital for Paralysis and Epilepsy.

1860   St. Peter's Hospital for Stone, London.
1861   National Dental Hospital.
1863   Hospital for Diseases of the Throat, London.
1866   Belgrave Hospital for Children and Grosvenor Hospital
       for Women.
1867   Queen's Hospital for Children.
1868   East London Hospital for Children.
1874   Central London Hospital for Throat, Nose and Ear.
1887   London Skin Hospital.

Although the London Fever Hospital was founded at the beginning of the century, many general hospitals continued to admit
fever cases into the same wards as non-infectious patients until as
late as 1860. Even the London Fever Hospital made no attempt to
distinguish between different types of fevers: sufferers from
typhus, enteric fever and scarlet fever were all accommodated in
the same ward. The isolation of fever patients met with very
strong opposition; it was stated that by concentrating the poison
in one ward or one building the danger of mortality was not
only increased among the patients, but also there was a greater
risk of spreading the infections.

The foundation of children's hospitals was also opposed; it was
considered essential for their mothers to care for them. In 1843
there were over two thousand patients in the hospitals of London,
but less than thirty of them were under the age of ten. Yet 21,000
children under the same age died in London each year. There
were, however, dispensaries for children and it was Dr. Charles
West, the physician at one of these, who started the movement
which led to the foundation of the Hospital for Sick Children in
Great Ormond Street. In the same decade children's hospitals
were established in Bristol, Norwich and Liverpool.

Dr. Lettsom's work in founding the Sea-Bathing Infirmary at
Margate had not been followed by any widespread provision for
the tuberculous. The general hospitals would not admit them
because of the lingering nature of the disease and the fact that it
was nearly always fatal—it caused the deaths of about one-third

of the population. Then in 1841 a poor clerk employed by a London firm of solicitors contracted tuberculosis. One of the partners made many unsuccessful attempts to get a hospital to accept him as a patient. This made the partner realise the lack of hospital accommodation for the unfortunate sufferers from consumption. He called together a few of his friends to discuss the matter, they issued a public appeal, and this led to the founding of the Brompton Hospital for Diseases of the Chest.

Over seventy special hospitals were founded between 1800 and 1860, and more than a hundred during the remaining forty years of the nineteenth century. The middle of the century also saw the establishment of a number of convalescent homes. These included the Metropolitan, Kingston Hill, London (1840), the Atkinson Morley, Wimbledon (1869) and Barnes Hospital, Cheadle (1875). Some of the convalescent homes were independent, others, such as the St. Bartholomew's Hospital Home at Swanley (1885), were attached to hospitals.

Until the middle of the century there still remained one class of sufferers for whom there was no hospital provision. These were the incurables. Neither the general nor the special hospitals would admit them, and they had to stay in their own homes, a great burden on their families, until 1854, when Dr. Andrew Reed founded the Royal Hospital and Home for Incurables at Putney.

The last forty years of the century saw a movement to set up hospitals where women might train for medicine, for the existing medical schools refused to allow them to study within their walls. The earliest of these hospitals was the New Hospital for Women (later the Elizabeth Garrett Anderson Hospital), which was founded by Elizabeth Garrett Anderson in 1872. Two years later the London School of Medicine for Women was founded.

While specialisation developed, the establishment of general hospitals continued throughout the country. A typical story of the founding of a general hospital to serve a market town and the surrounding rural district is that of the Taunton and Somerset Hospital.

In 1809 one of the town's general practitioners wrote to a local

A Surgical Operation and Heating the Surgeon's Instruments, from the Early Twelfth-century *Astronomia medica*

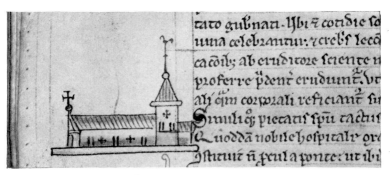

St. John's Hospital, Oxford, erected in 1233, from a Fifteenth-century MS.

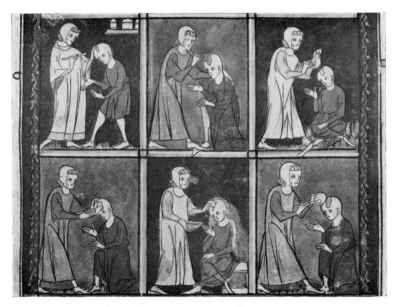

Six Stages in a Brain Operation, from a medieval MS.

The Pest-house at Odiham, Hampshire

A Thirteenth-century Hospital

Hospital, Middlesex, by Rowlandson and Pugin

(From *The Microcosm of London*

Rahere Ward, St. Bartholomew's Hospital in 1832, from a
contemporary drawing

A Ward in the Hampstead Smallpox Hospital, 1870

St. Thomas's Hospital on the Albert Embankment. Opened by
Queen Victoria, 21st June, 1871

Princess Mary Ward, East London Hospital for Children,
1878

Waiting to see the Doctor at the Seamen's Hospital Dispensary,
London Docks, 1881

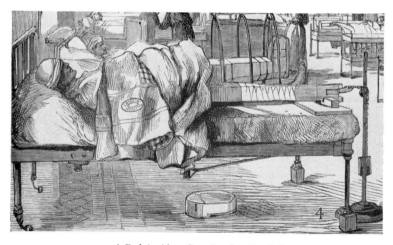

A Bad Accident Case, London Hospital

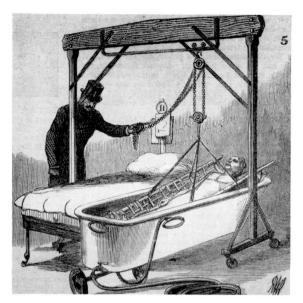

The Bath Lift, Middlesex Hospital

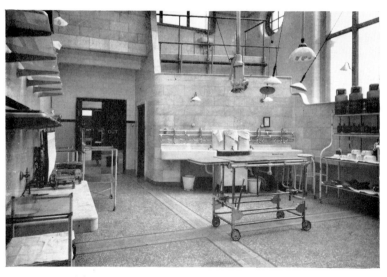

The Operating Theatre, London Hospital, about 1900

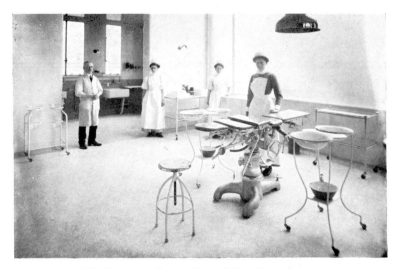

The Operating Theatre, King's College Hospital, 1914

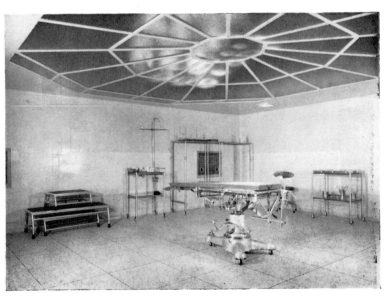

The Operating Theatre, Maida Vale Hospital.
(This operating theatre was opened in 1956)

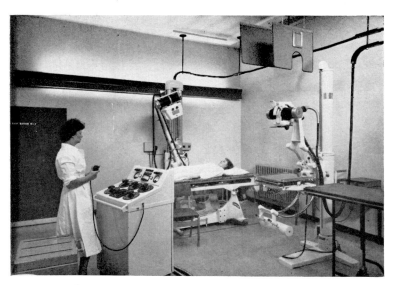

Part of the X-ray Department of the City General Hospital, Sheffield.
(This department was opened in 1959)

The Children's Waiting-room in the Out-Patients' Department of St
James's Hospital, Balham
(This department was completed in 1957)

Nurses' Station, Cubicle Block, West Cumberland Hospital

Male Geriatric Bed Ward, West Cumberland Hospital

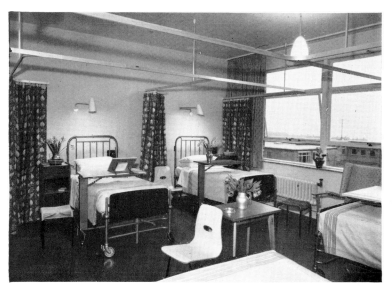

Geriatric Bed Ward, West Cumberland Hospital

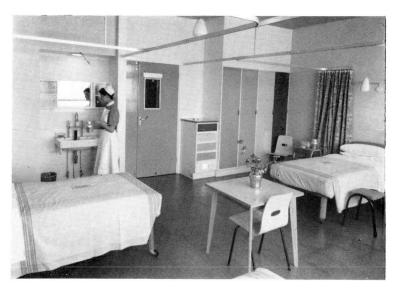

Geriatric Four-bed Ward, West Cumberland Hospital

The West Cumberland Hospital as it will appear when completed in 1964

newspaper suggesting that a meeting should be called on the day on which the jubilee of George III was being celebrated. The purpose of the meeting should be "to take into consideration the best and most effectual plan for establishing in Taunton a public Medical Institution, for the use of its poorer inhabitants." The doctor's proposal met with a good response, and at the meeting a committee of local gentlemen was formed. In less than ten weeks a plan of the hospital had been prepared and adopted, and a little over two years later the first patients were admitted.

The realisation of the need for specialisation was not accompanied by any great improvements in the standards of treatment. The doctors still relied largely on leeches; in fact the number of these used increased rapidly. At Bart's in 1821 the consumption was 24,700, in 1822 it was 52,000, and by 1837 it was 96,300. They were used for all sorts of ailments.

In many cases bleeding was the method by which doctors brought their patients to a state of near unconsciousness before anaesthetics became available. The patient sat in a chair and a vein in his arm was opened. The blood was allowed to flow until he had lost so much that he was almost unconscious. Then, when he was incapable of resistance and almost unable to feel any pain, the doctor would replace a dislocated limb.

In 1811 a patient wrote an account of his experience in undergoing an operation without an anaesthetic. The operation was for the removal of a stone from the bladder. This is what he wrote—

My habit and constitution being good it required little preparation of body, and my mind was made up. When all parties had arrived I retired to my room for a minute, bent my knee in silent adoration and submission and returning to the surgeons conducted them to the apartment in which the preparations had been made. The bandages etc. having been adjusted I was prepared to receive a shock of pain of extreme violence and so much had I over-rated it, that the first incision did not even make me wince although I had declared that it was not my intention to restrain such impulse, convinced that such effort of restraint could only lead to additional exhaustion. At subsequent moments therefore I did cry out under the pain, but was allowed to have gone through the operation with great firmness.

The forcing up of the staff prior to the introduction of the gorget gave me the first real pain, but this instantly subsided after the incision of the bladder was made, the rush of the urine appeared to relieve it and soothe the wound.

When the forceps was introduced the pain was again very considerable and every movement of the instrument in endeavouring to find the stone increased it. Still, however, my mind was firm and confident, and, although anxious, I was yet alive to what was going on. After several ineffectual attempts to grasp the stone I heard the operator say in the lowest whisper, "It is a little awkward, it lies under my hand. Give me the curved forceps," upon which he withdrew the others. Here, I think, I asked if there was anything wrong— or something to that purport—and was reanimated by the reply conveyed in the kindest manner, "Be patient, sir, it will soon be over." When the other forceps was introduced I had again to undergo the searching for the stone and heard Mr. Cline (the surgeon) say, "I have got it." I had probably by this time conceived that the worst was over, but when the necessary force was applied to withdraw the stone the sensation was such as I cannot find words to describe. In addition to the positive pain there was something peculiar in the feel. The bladder embraced the stone as firmly as the stone was itself grasped by the forceps; it seemed as if the whole organ was about to be torn out. The duration, however, of this really trying part of the operation was short and when the words "Now, sir, it is all over" struck my ear, the ejaculation of "Thank God! Thank God!" was uttered with a fervency and fulness of heart which can only be conceived. I am quite unable to describe my sensations at the moment. There was a feeling of release, not from the pain of the operation, for that was gone and lost sight of, but from my enemy and tormentor with a lightness and buoyance of spirits, elating my imagination to the belief that I was restored to perfect health as if by a miracle.

Sir James Simpson published his pamphlet about the discovery of chloroform in 1847, and it was used at Bart's within a week. They had not been so quick in adopting other new remedies and treatments; very little cod liver oil was used there until 1846, five years after its value had been made known. Castor oil had been a popular remedy much earlier—popular with the doctors, if not with patients! The out-patients at the Westminster Hospital found a way of getting rid of theirs and at the same time adding to their incomes. In 1822 it was recorded that the committee "strongly recommends to the Medical Gentlemen that in future the Castor Oil delivered to the Out-Patients be mixed with some colouring matter to prevent the sale of it, which hath lately been discovered."

For bandages many hospitals used linen rags made by tearing up old sheets. When there were not enough sheets, appeals were made to the local public to donate rags. Even as late as 1869 the Radcliffe Infirmary at Oxford issued an advertisement asking for rags for use in dressing wounds.

The difficulties of performing operations without anaesthetics was one of the reasons why surgery was carried out much less frequently than it is now. At the Manchester Royal Infirmary during 1833 there were only 110 operations, consisting of forty amputations of the leg, twenty-two amputations of the arm, eight hernias, eight tumours, seven lithotomies, six contractures after burns, nine cataracts, three trepans, two aneurysms, two tracheotomies, one hare-lip, and two described as "various."

Antiseptic surgery had not been introduced. After an operation the wound was sewn up with black horsehair; a large leash of this was hung in the theatre. If the operation was only a minor one, the surgeon wore his ordinary clothes; if the operation was of a major nature, he made one slight change: he took off his ordinary coat and replaced it with a dirty old black cloth coat kept for the purpose.

Under these conditions it is not to be wondered at that many of the operations were fatal. During the years 1838 and 1839 there were 143 operations at the Manchester Royal Infirmary and thirty-six of these resulted in the deaths of the patients. The surgeons realised that in making up their minds to operate they were reaching a very serious decision. One of them wrote to *The Times* in 1829 suggesting that "in every case of dangerous operation or one of questionable expediency the principal surgeons and consulting surgeons do hold a conference in the presence of their pupils and determine by a majority of the votes of such surgeons the measures to be adopted."

Sometimes, of course, mistakes were made even in minor matters. In 1838 a gentleman wrote to St. George's Hospital, Hyde Park Corner, complaining that when his servant had gone there because of toothache, the wrong tooth had been extracted and then "replaced most carefully in a wrong position, the hind part being placed before."

There had been little improvement in the patients' dietaries. A diet sheet printed for the Radcliffe Infirmary, Oxford, in 1820, shows that their meals were as follows—

Sunday and Thursday

Breakfast Water gruel or milk pottage, 1 pt.
Dinner Veal or mutton, boiled, 8 ozs.
Supper Sunday—cheese, 2 ozs., or butter, 1 oz. Thursday—
Water gruel, milk pottage or broth, 1 pt.

Monday and Friday

Breakfast Milk pottage, water gruel or broth, 1 pt.
Dinner Rice-milk, 1 pt.
Supper Cheese, 2 ozs., or butter, 1 oz.

Tuesday and Saturday

Breakfast Water gruel or milk pottage, 1 pt.
Dinner Mutton or beef, boiled, 8 ozs.
Supper Water gruel, milk pottage or broth, 1 pt.

Wednesday

Breakfast Milk pottage or water gruel, 1 pt.
Dinner Bread pudding, baked, 12 ozs.
Supper Cheese, 2 ozs., or butter, 1 oz.
Beer 1 qt. a day on Sunday, Monday, Wednesday and Friday, and $1\frac{1}{2}$ pts. a day on Tuesday, Thursday and Saturday.
Bread As much as each patient desired.

Like many hospitals, the Radcliffe Infirmary had its own brew-house and bakehouse. The porter did the brewing, while the bread was baked twice weekly by a baker who was paid half a crown a day. Small beer was brewed for the patients and ale for the staff. Strong beer, which was used for poultices, was purchased from local brewers. Bread was also required for poultices, and in 1852 over 240 lb. were consumed in this manner. After the poultices had been used, they were dug into the garden as manure.

The food was so poor that it had to be supplemented by gifts from the patients' friends and relations, or by items which the patients bought, if they could afford to do so. Each patient had a box under his bed in which he kept his belongings and in 1839 a complaint was entered in the Visitors' Book that these boxes often contained an assortment of foodstuffs—bacon, cheese, butter, bread, cakes, apples and slices of meat were mentioned. In some hospitals food-sellers were allowed to go around the wards; at Guy's a man sold watercress and periwinkles every afternoon.

Although the equipment still left much to be desired, there were some improvements. At Bart's iron bedsteads were provided in 1815. Five years later a slipper bath was purchased at the Westminster Hospital, but apparently the patients could have only cold baths, for in 1828 when the question of hot baths was considered, it was pointed out that the water would have to be carried upstairs in cans. In 1821 a cold shower was provided. Gas lighting was installed in 1820. The governors of the Westminster were well ahead of Bart's in thinking of iron bedsteads, for they appointed a sub-committee to consider the matter in 1805. However, as it took this committee sixteen years to reach a decision, Bart's had been using iron bedsteads for six years before there were any at the Westminster. The governors of the Westminster were very proud of their new hospital, which was opened in 1834. Among its most important features, they thought, were the water-closets. However, no modern hospital staff would have been pleased with them, for they were separated from the wards only by a thin board partition. Moreover, one of them leaked through the floor on to food being prepared in the kitchen below! There were no water-closets or any type of sanitary accommodation for out-patients, and it was not until 1858 that any was provided.

The mattresses were filled with straw. In 1821 a House Visitor complained that those at the Radcliffe Infirmary, Oxford, were never changed, so an instruction was issued that the covers should be washed regularly and filled with clean straw. There were also complaints about the sheets. Another House Visitor remarked: "The sheets are half washed, and some of them in the store room smell disagreeably of oil or ointment. The matron says they are sometimes worn a month; surely that is much too long." At the London Hospital a few feather beds were purchased in 1820. As late as the eighteen-forties double beds were still in use at the Manchester Royal Infirmary.

The patients had no crockery or knives and forks. The plates and dishes were of pewter. In 1840 the governors of the Manchester Royal Infirmary agreed to allow the patients "to have the use of knives and forks to their meals." Six years earlier the following minute had been passed by the governors of the Nottingham General Hospital: "Resolved: that 2 tablespoons, 4 desert [sic] spoons, and one teaspoon be purchased; added to those already in the house, will make 4 tablespoons, 4 desert spoons, and six teaspoons. The matron holding herself responsible for the safety of the above articles."

There was still strict segregation of the sexes as far as the patients were concerned, although the rules were of course broken, much to the concern of the hospital authorities. In 1840 it was proposed that a new hospital should be built in York, and one of the reasons put forward in support of this suggestion was that "the separating of the sexes, both in the house and the airing grounds, is not as complete as it ought to be." Eight years later the matron of the Taunton and Somerset Hospital was instructed "to take care that the Male and Female Patients take exercise at separate times and be not in the Garden at the same time on any occasion."

Until the eighteen-twenties—and even later in some hospitals—candles were the only form of illumination. Even operations had to be carried out by candlelight. At the London Hospital each ward was allowed seven candles a week. When the governors asked the surgeons and physicians for their opinion on the introduction of gas lighting, they would not agree to it in the wards, but only in the theatre and the corridors.

In the provision of better equipment, the staff were not entirely overlooked. In 1824 a carpet was provided for the secretary of the Worcester Royal Infirmary. The matron was also given one, but hers was second-hand!

At many hospitals the arrangements for seeing out-patients were far from good. At the Bristol Royal Infirmary their waiting-room was so crowded that the atmosphere was described as "tainted and poisonous." The patients were examined in two rooms, one for medical and the other for surgical cases, but no attempt was made to sort them into these two categories before-hand. Consequently, when the attendants came to summon patients to the consulting rooms, there was a mad struggle to be the next to see the doctors. There were several medical men in both of the consulting rooms, each of them attending to a patient at the same time. The sexes were not segregated, so that often men and women were examined together.

The overall administration of the hospitals continued to be in the hands of the governors or trustees, who held their posts because of the contributions they made to the funds. Each governor was entitled to a vote on every question, no matter how trivial it was. Sometimes several hundred governors turned up at a board meeting. It was gradually realised that smaller bodies would deal with the business far more expeditiously, and so committees were appointed. This idea sometimes met with opposition. At the Westminster, for example, it was first suggested in 1801, but it was rejected because it "withdrew privileges from the trustees," and the unwieldy system of administration continued until 1835, when a house committee was appointed.

One of the governors' privileges at most hospitals was to authorise the admission of patients. A person wanting to be admitted had first to obtain a letter from a governor. No matter how serious his illness or how urgent his need for treatment, he would not be allowed in the hospital unless he could produce a governor's letter. The only alternative was to deposit a certain sum to pay for his funeral; if he recovered, this was refunded to him. This absurd system actually led to the foundation of one of London's best-known hospitals. One night in 1828 Dr. William Marsden was going home when he found an eighteen-year-old girl on the steps of Holborn church. She was critically ill, but because she had been unable to produce money or a governor's letter, she had been refused admission to St. Bartholomew's Hospital. Marsden befriended the girl and started a campaign against the system of governors' letters. He opened a small dispensary where the poor could receive treatment without payment or any formalities, and this gradually developed into the Royal Free Hospital.

Some hospitals made charges for certain types of patients. In 1821 it was decided to charge not less than 7s. 6d. a week for all patients at the Worcester Royal Infirmary "who may be brought in from accidents occasioned by the improper and furious driving of public carriages, or vehicles of any description." Even in those days road accidents caused concern! In 1834 the governors of St. George's Hospital, Hyde Park Corner, were perturbed by the number of patients admitted "after accidents from omnibuses and cabriolets."

The governors often made regulations about an amazing variety of matters, frequently quite trivial ones. The rules drawn at the Worcester Royal Infirmary in 1821 included the following—

(*a*) Matron to treat the patients with kindness and civility.
(*b*) Patients to wash their hands and faces every morning and their feet every Saturday night.
(*c*) Nurses not to throw out of the windows any dirt, tow or rags.
(*d*) Nurses not to allow the patients' clothes to be hung out of the ward windows.

It was customary at most hospitals for the members of the House Committee to take it in turns to visit the hospital to ensure that the rules were observed. At the Radcliffe Infirmary, Oxford, the House Visitors had to inquire "whether the patients be duly attended; whether the patients or servants have been guilty of Swearing, Drunkenness, any Immorality or Indecency; whether the Provisions be good; and whether any have been carried out or brought into the patients clandestinely; and that they enter what they think observable in a Book provided for that purpose." The visitors even took it upon themselves to censor the patients' reading matter. One of the entries made in the "Book provided" during 1841 is as follows: "Saw the *Sunday Observer*, an abominable paper for the perusal of a sick ward, in the centre attic. Whose business is it to keep such papers from the patients?"

During the first sixty years of the nineteenth century the standards of the nursing profession remained very low. The nurses were, for the most part, ignorant and untrained, and more interested in ruining themselves with gin than in improving the health and comfort of their patients. Many of them closely resembled Dickens' Sairey Gamp in their behaviour. The better nurses were employed during the day, while at night the patients were left to the care of "watchers," who knew nothing of nursing and could hardly be expected to devote much attention to their duties for the few pence they received for a night's work. A few hospital authorities realised that the wages they paid would not attract good staff. In 1838 the committee of the Middlesex Hospital expressed the opinion "that a hope may be entertained by raising the wages . . . of procuring and retaining the better description of nurses—women who will take more interest in their duties, their character and their appearance." The wages of the nurses at Bristol Royal Infirmary were increased from £12 to £16 a year in 1849, and then they were raised gradually to £20.

The conditions under which they had to work, as well as their wages, needed improvement. At many hospitals they had no dining-rooms and had to take their meals as best they could. Often a nurse's dinner was only a rasher of bacon which she had cooked herself by holding it on a piece of wood in front of the fire, and she had to eat it in the scullery or in the ward.

The London Hospital also tried to raise the standard of their nurses. In 1822 it was decided not to appoint nurses who were unable to read or write. However, in 1829 the governors found there were not enough literate women who wanted to be nurses, so they had to modify their resolution and state that in future only nurses who could read or write should administer medicines. When the Brompton Hospital was opened in 1842 the following rules were made regarding nurses: "No nurse shall be taken on trial without a proper character for honesty, sobriety and kindness; and no nurse shall be permanently hired till she had been at least three weeks upon trial, nor unless she is able to read handwriting. The nurses shall be answerable for the cleanliness, quietness and good order of the wards, and shall clean the rooms and passages assigned to the care of each of them respectively, and have them in a proper state by nine o'clock in the morning; they shall wash and take to the dispensary daily the phials and gallipots that have been used, and shall pay prompt attention to the cleanliness of the linen and bedding of each of the patients, and shall inform the matron of any change that is required before the ordinary time."

There was considerable variation in the rates of pay of nurses, even in the same district. In 1838 the wages at three London hospitals were as follows—

St. Thomas's—sisters £37 a year, nurses 9s. 7d. a week plus beer; Guy's—sisters £50, nurses £30; St. George's—sisters £21, nurses £16, but both grades were allowed 6 lbs. of bread weekly, 2 pts. of beer daily, and 1s. 0d. a day for board wages.

The nurse had no pension to look forward to when she became too old to work. Occasionally a committee would make a small gratuity to a nurse who had given many years of hard and faithful service, but she might even have to appeal to them for this. In the annual accounts of Worcester Royal Infirmary for the year 1832, under the heading "Night nurse," there is an entry "Allowance to old ditto." This records the sum of 2s. 6d. a week which was granted to Sarah Pilkington after she had sent the following letter to the committee:

> Honble. Gentlemen,
>   I take this freedom of addressing these few lines to you, in hopes that your Honourable Board will take it into consideration to allow me some small allowance for a subsistence—as I am now 73 years of age—and I served as night nurse in the Infirmary for upwards of 20 years, and I am now past my labours and incapable of any means of support and by so doing your petitioner will be ever bound to pray for you—and am your humble servant.

Twenty-five years earlier the committee had sent Sarah Pilkington's predecessor to the workhouse because she had become so old and infirm that she could no longer do her work. They could not find anybody else to act as night nurse, so they ordered each of the other nurses (apparently there were only four of them) to remain on duty every fourth night.

The sisters' salaries given above seem very low, but they were better than those of some matrons. In 1831 the matron of Nottingham General Hospital received only £30—less than the chaplain and only half the apothecary's salary. Most matrons were married women or widows; the Westminster did not have an unmarried matron until 1848. Some committees considered appointing single matrons much earlier than this. In 1822 the matron of Worcester Royal Infirmary died and it was decided that her successor must be a spinster or a widow, between thirty-five and fifty years of age, free from encumbrance, of strictly moral habits, of active, domestic and humane disposition, and able to keep the accounts.

By the eighteen-thirties most of the more important hospitals had a steward. One was appointed at St. George's in 1826. Six years later the Westminster had its first steward, and numerous duties were assigned to him, including a daily visit to the wards and the prevention of smoking throughout the hospital. He also had to remain in the hospital always, unless the apothecary or the matron was there.

At some hospitals the steward was already known as the

secretary, although at most places the former title lasted well into the present century. One of the hospitals which had a secretary was the Manchester Royal Infirmary. His salary in 1802 was sixty guineas, the same as that of the apothecary; both officers were also provided with board and lodging. The salaries varied considerably in different parts of the country. At the Nottingham General Hospital the apothecary received £60, but the secretary there was paid only half this amount. The Governors of the London Hospital were particularly generous towards their senior administrative official. It is true that they required him to carry out the duties of chaplain as well as those of secretary, but they made his post sound very important by calling it "House governor" and in 1818 they were paying him £250, in addition to providing board and residence. Less than fifty years later this had been increased to £650, plus eight per cent of the fees received from pupils, plus a large house, plus 36 tons of coal, plus 942 gallons of porter—a total which seems to justify one of the governors calling him "the best paid official in Europe!"

The apothecary was usually fairly well paid, although it must be admitted that his duties were more onerous than those of the modern hospital pharmacist. In addition to making up the medicines, he had to be in clinical charge of the patients when none of the visiting physicians or surgeons were on the premises. He was also in charge of the students, and received part of their fees. At most hospitals he was required to be resident. The London Hospital did not treat its apothecary as generously as its secretary, and required him to ensure the cleanliness of the heads, feet and legs of all patients being admitted, examine their clothes for vermin, superintend the heating and ventilation, and submit a report to the committee every week on the behaviour of the nurses. As if this was not enough, he had to go to chapel daily! When the poor man objected to carrying water for the hot bath, he was reprimanded. Although he was resident, he was not provided with a room of his own, and had to sleep on a settee-bed in the physician's parlour.

As mentioned above, at the London Hospital the posts of

secretary and chaplain were combined. In 1821 the governors of
Worcester Royal Infirmary decided to try another combination—
when the house surgeon resigned they advertised for a secretary-
house surgeon at a salary of £110 15s. 0d., with board and
lodging. (The appointment was never made, because the house
surgeon withdrew his resignation.)

The appointment of a physician or surgeon was often a very
expensive affair for the applicants. Vacancies were filled by
elections, at which all the trustees were entitled to vote, and
frequently several hundred turned up to do so. The rival candidates canvassed for support, in a similar manner to politicians
contesting a seat in a parliamentary election. When a surgeon
was to be appointed at the Manchester Royal Infirmary in 1835
there were four candidates. No fewer than nine hundred trustees
met in the Town Hall to vote, and the ballot lasted three hours.
The successful candidate spent nearly £700 to secure his victory;
a large part of this sum was to meet the cost of transporting voters
from the surrounding countryside.

In the larger hospitals each surgeon had several dressers and one
of these was always on duty. He had to dress the wounds of the
patients, attend to all casualties, and draw teeth whenever
dentistry was required. If there was an emergency, he had to
decide whether or not to send for the surgeon. At all hospitals
the surgeons and physicians were allowed to have apprentices,
but the number of these was limited. At the Worcester Royal
Infirmary the house surgeon was permitted to have only one
apprentice, who had to stay at least five years. A premium of
£250 was demanded, and payments of £20 at the beginning of
the apprenticeship and £10 at the end of the first three years.
The hospital provided the apprentice with board, lodging and
laundry. At St. George's Hospital only those students who contributed to the microscope fund were allowed to use the microscope. It was the practice for parties to be held to celebrate the
arrival of a new student or the departure of one at the end of his
apprenticeship, but apparently these became a little too rowdy,
for the governors decreed that "the supper parties which it has

been customary to give in the hospital by the officers on their entrance or their departure be discontinued." The average age for commencing an apprenticeship was sixteen, although one of the surgeons at Guy's had been an apprentice when he was only fourteen. Guy's, like many other hospitals, had a proper medical school by the middle of the century. Until 1825 they had an arrangement with St. Thomas's Hospital whereby students of one hospital were admitted to the practice of the other. Then a dispute over the appointment of a lecturer led the governors of Guy's to establish their own medical school. The normal length of time spent at the school was only twelve months, and so the programme of study had to be carefully planned to ensure that the times of the lectures did not clash. Because of this, the student's working day was often a very long one: his first lecture might begin at 7.45 a.m. and his last not until 8 p.m. In addition to the fee paid to the hospital authorities, payments had to be made to each lecturer. Some of this money was used by the lecturers to pay for prizes which they awarded to their best pupils.

Not all surgeons and physicians were so keen to encourage their students; in fact, some of them even reproved the students if they dared to ask questions during the ward rounds, and did not give them any instruction whatsoever. One doctor who was trained at Bart's in the eighteen-twenties later wrote: "I cannot recollect having got a single useful lesson in the treatment of disease from the three physicians of St. Bartholomew's Hospital." The teaching which the students received in the lecture-room was often of little more value than the instruction given to them on the wards. The students frequently interrupted the lecturer with catcalls, fireworks, and the playing of various musical instruments, so that he was sometimes reduced to telling them obscene stories in order to hold their attention. Such behaviour on the part of both students and lecturer was taken as a matter of course. A leading medical man of the nineteenth century, writing of his student days, said: "It was not, generally, thought amiss that one of my teachers told many stories, some of which were obscene, some very nasty."

An important step forward in the teaching of medicine was taken in 1828 with the foundation of University College, London. It was established for the purpose of giving instruction in the arts, science and medicine. Less than ten years later its own hospital was opened—the first to be built especially for teaching purposes.

For many of those who had the misfortune to need hospital treatment during the nineteenth century the only place available was the workhouse infirmary. Most of the workhouses were established following the passing of the Poor Law Amendment Act of 1834. The Act discouraged the provision of anything more than the bare necessities of life, for in order to prevent the abuse of poor relief it set up the principle of "less eligibility." Nothing must be done to make the condition of the pauper more eligible than "the situation of the independent labourer of the lowest sort." Although there might be some justification for this harsh doctrine in the case of able-bodied men, it was quite heartless to apply it to the sick and the aged. Yet that was what was done, and the miserable inhabitants of the workhouse infirmaries had to exist under appalling conditions.

The wards were insanitary and often overcrowded. The patients had to wear the same clothing and use the same bedding for weeks on end. The number of such articles as towels and brushes and combs was usually quite insufficient. Medical and nursing attention were totally inadequate. Often there was no resident medical officer and a doctor made only one short visit to the infirmary each week. The nursing was carried out by some of the able-bodied workhouse inmates, who had no training or aptitude for the work, and did it only because they were told to and because they were rewarded with beer and gin. They were mostly elderly women; at the Strand Workhouse there were eighteen pauper nurses, all over sixty, and two of them were so infirm that, even when assisting each other, they could not lift a patient up in bed. Often the nurses could not read the directions on the medicine bottles, and even if they could read they ignored them. At Shoreditch Infirmary a nurse admitted that she gave the patients medicine "irrespective of directions, three times, twice or once a day, according to her own opinion of the cases." Little attempt was made to separate the various types of cases: patients suffering from smallpox and typhus were mixed with those who had non-infectious ailments.

Some improvements might have been expected as a result of the passing of the Sanitary Act of 1866 and the Public Health Act of 1875, which permitted local authorities to establish general hospitals. Yet only three councils—Barry, Bradford and Willesden—made use of the powers granted by these Acts. In 1910 Sidney and Beatrice Webb reported that "a majority of the rural district authorities and not a few urban district authorities have no hospital accommodation even for the most infectious diseases."

In London, however, there were considerable improvements. The public conscience had been roused sufficiently for the formation, in 1866, of the Association for the Improvement of the Infirmaries of London Workhouses. In the following year the Metropolitan Poor Act was passed. This set up the Metropolitan Asylums Board to provide and maintain hospitals for the insane poor and for those suffering from all kinds of illness.

The Board established separate hospitals for infectious and non-infectious diseases, tuberculosis and smallpox. The example set in London was followed slowly in other parts of the country, and in this way the Metropolitan Poor Act had an important place in the history of English hospitals.

CHAPTER VII

YEARS OF REFORM

BY the middle of the nineteenth century there were already the first signs that long-needed reforms in the voluntary hospitals were on the way. In 1829 the poet Southey wrote to his friend Mrs. Amelia Opie "to engage her sympathies and those of Mrs. Fry in the establishment of Societies for reforming the internal management of Hospitals and Infirmaries, so as to do for the hospitals what Mrs. Fry had already done for the prisons." Elizabeth Fry had realised the need for great changes in the hospitals: she had mentioned the matter in a book published in 1827. But her other work kept her so busy that it was not until 1840 that she was able to take any practical steps. Then she opened a training home for nurses in London.

Twenty young women, carefully selected, were trained in one of the larger hospitals. When their training was completed they were regarded as Nursing Sisters, although the public usually called them Fry Nurses. They lived at the home and were paid an annual salary. There was even a fund to provide them with pensions, provided they continued to work a certain number of years. Yet, although they had been trained in hospitals, none of their work was done in hospitals. They went to the homes of sick people and did all their nursing there.

The reform of hospital nursing commenced with the foundation in London in 1848 of the "Training Institution for Nurses in Hospitals, Families and for the Poor," or St. John's House, as it was usually called, from the name of the parish in which it was situated. Its aims were made quite clear—

It is proposed to establish a corporate or collegiate institution, the objects of which would be to maintain in a community women who are members of the Church of England, who should receive such instruction and undergo such training as might best fit them to act as nurses and visitors to the sick and poor. It is proposed to connect the institution with some hospital or hospitals, in which the women under training or those who had already been educated, might find the opportunity of exercising their calling or of acquiring experience. It is absolutely necessary that the proposed establishment should be a religious one, and that all connected with it should regard the work in which they are embarked as a religious work.

The probationers commenced their training at the age of eighteen. They were trained for two years at the Middlesex Hospital or the Westminster Hospital. During this period they were paid £15 annually. At the end of the two years, provided they were regarded as satisfactory, they became "Nurses." By 1856 they were able to take over the whole of the nursing of King's College Hospital.

A similar institution was the All Saints' Sisterhood, which was founded in 1851. It established a home for incurable women, and for thirty-seven years, commencing in 1862, supplied all the nursing staff of King's College Hospital.

It was a war which led to the most sweeping reforms, however. In 1854 Miss Florence Nightingale went to Scutari to superintend the nursing of the sick and wounded in the Crimean War. She came of a wealthy family, but the way of life of a rich Victorian young lady did not appeal to her. By the time she reached the age of twenty-four she had realised that her vocation was "to devote herself to works of charity in hospitals." When she told her parents that she wanted to spend three months in a hospital learning nursing they were horrified. They, like most people of their class, regarded nursing as one of the lowliest professions, fit only for the worst type of women. Nurses were noted for drunkenness and immorality. Parental opposition prevented Florence from carrying out her plan then, but it did not stifle her ambition. She read all she could about hospitals and about nursing, and in 1850, when she was thirty, she spent a fortnight at the Institution of Deaconesses at Kaiserswerth on the Rhine. This had been founded in 1836 by Pastor Fliedner as a training establishment for young ladies wishing to learn nursing. The following year she went there again for several months. In 1853 she was offered the post of

Superintendent of the Institution for the Care of Sick Gentle-women in Distressed Circumstances. This Institution was in need of reorganisation. Florence reorganised it very successfully, and then carried on with other nursing work, including the care of cholera patients at the Middlesex Hospital. In 1854 her friend Sidney Herbert, the Secretary of War, who knew of her work, asked her to go to Scutari. The reports of *The Times* war correspondent on the conditions there had caused an outcry throughout England. There were no nurses to care for our soldiers, and comparison was naturally made with the French, whose surgeons were assisted by Sisters of Charity. The correspondent described the Sisters as "devoted women" and "excellent nurses."

Florence Nightingale took a party of nurses with her to Scutari. She made drastic changes. She took the control of the nursing staff out of the hands of the army authorities, and saw that women were made responsible for this work. On her initiative the sick and wounded soldiers were provided with such essential items as soap, towels and toothbrushes; it is amazing to record, but the army's principal medical officer was actually of the opinion that a soldier had no need of a toothbrush! By these and many other similar acts she became the British soldiers' heroine. By the time she returned to England at the end of 1856 she was the heroine of the whole nation.

The people wanted to show their appreciation of her work, so a fund was launched, and it was suggested that the money should be used to found a school for nurses. Miss Nightingale welcomed this idea, but because of the state of her health she felt unable to become superintendent of the school herself. However, she supervised all the arrangements for the Nightingale School of Nursing, which was opened at St. Thomas's Hospital in 1860. St. Thomas's was chosen because Mrs. Wardroper, the matron there, was outstandingly efficient, and noted for the manner in which she controlled her staff. She was Superintendent of the Nightingale Training School until 1887.

The most revolutionary feature of the Nightingale training scheme was the placing of the nurses under the direct control of the matron. Previously they had been under the charge of the medical officers. Many of the doctors were violently opposed to the scheme because it took the nursing staff out of their control. One of the surgeons at St. Thomas's wrote to *The Times*: "That this proposed hospital nurse-training scheme has not met with the approbation and support of the medical profession is beyond doubt. The very small number of medical men whose names appear in the enormous list of subscribers to the Fund cannot have passed unnoticed. Only three physicians and one surgeon from one hospital and one physician from a second are found among the supporters." He went on to say that he could see no need for any improvement in the type of nurse being employed, and in his opinion it was quite unnecessary to give her all the training that was proposed: "As regards the nurses or wardmaids, these are in much the same position as housemaids and require little teaching beyond that of poultice making."

The probationers in the Nightingale School were paid £10 a year by the fund, which also provided them with board, lodging, laundry and uniform. They lived in the hospital, where an upper floor of one wing was adapted for them. Each of them had a separate bedroom. They shared a sitting-room, and two rooms were set aside for the sister in charge. This was the first nurses' home in an English hospital. The probationers' uniform consisted of a brown dress with a white cap and apron. Their training lasted for a year and at the end of each month Mrs. Wardroper had to complete a "Monthly Sheet of Personal Character and Acquirements" in respect of each nurse. This form had been drawn up by Florence Nightingale.

At the end of the year's training the probationers became nurses either at St. Thomas's or at some other hospital. In this way Florence Nightingale's ideas spread gradually to all the other hospitals in the country, and her four main principles were widely adopted. These principles were as follows—

1. The matron was responsible for all the nursing in the hospital, and for the appointment and dismissal of the nursing staff.

2. The probationers must live at the hospital to ensure that discipline was maintained.

3. They must be given theoretical teaching, including instruction in the basic sciences, by the medical staff, and must receive practical teaching in the wards under the supervision of the sisters.

4. The importance of the ward sisters must be clearly recognised.

Despite the opposition of the medical profession, the training scheme proved a great success and slowly led to the complete reformation of hospital nursing. This was, of course, largely due to the careful planning of Florence Nightingale, but the work of Mrs. Wardroper during the twenty-seven years that she was superintendent of the school must not be overlooked. Without her wise supervision the scheme might well have failed.

It was not only the nursing service that Florence Nightingale reformed. She attacked the appalling conditions which led to the very high mortality rate in hospitals. In her *Notes on Hospitals*, published in 1859, she stated: "It may seem a strange principle to enunciate as the very first requirement in a Hospital that it should do the sick no harm. It is quite necessary nevertheless to lay down such a principle, because the actual mortality in hospitals, especially those of large crowded cities, is very much higher than any calculation founded on the mortality of the same class of patient treated *out* of hospital would lead us to expect." She believed that disease was caused by dirt, and she was a great advocate of cleanliness and fresh air.

Florence Nightingale's *Notes on Hospitals* revolutionised the whole theory of hospital management and hospital construction. Instead of massive single buildings she advocated the pavilion type of structure, where there would be better light and ventilation, and the number of people under a single roof would be much less, thus diminishing the risks of cross-infection. An opportunity soon came for a great London hospital to be constructed according to her ideas. The proposed route for the South Eastern Railway between London Bridge and Charing Cross was right across St.

Thomas's Hospital. Florence Nightingale was consulted and on her advice the hospital was rebuilt in Lambeth. It was constructed in the pavilion style which she had advocated, and this was to prove very satisfactory.

The adoption of Florence Nightingale's reforms took place only gradually. They were accepted more readily in the voluntary hospitals than in the Poor Law infirmaries. These were the only institutions which would admit poor people who required long periods of treatment or who were suffering from incurable diseases. The conditions in them were so bad that people usually went to them only as a last resort. The only nursing they received during the daytime was rendered by pauper women who were inmates of the workhouse, and at night the wards were usually locked up and the patients were left without any attention whatever.

It was not until 1865 that the first step was taken to improve the standard of nursing in these institutions. William Rathbone, a Liverpool philanthropist, offered to meet the cost of employing trained nurses at the Brownlow Hill Infirmary for three years. The Board of Guardians hesitated about accepting his offer, but eventually decided that his scheme should be tried in the male wards. There were to be a dozen nurses trained at St. Thomas's Hospital and a dozen probationers carefully selected from the young women of the city. The other nurses would be the best of the workhouse inmates, but they would be paid wages and would no longer be regarded as paupers. They would all be under the direction of a Lady Superintendent.

Rathbone asked Florence Nightingale to choose the Lady Superintendent and she selected an Irishwoman, Agnes Jones. When Miss Jones commenced her task she found that it was not unusual for the bedclothes to be used for months without being washed and for the men to wear the same shirts for six or seven weeks. The infirmary was very crowded, and sometimes there were two or even three patients in a single bed. Miss Jones soon remedied this state of affairs, and within two years the Board of Guardians decided that the employment of trained nurses must be continued. One part of the experiment was a failure, however. It was found impossible to train the pauper women to do nursing work. Apart from this, Rathbone's plan was successful, and soon other Poor Law infirmaries were employing trained nurses.

The working conditions of the nurses were also improved by relieving them of such duties as scrubbing floors. At Guy's this step was taken in 1857 and other women were employed for this work. At the same time the number of nurses was reduced, for the governors argued that if a nurse did not have to spend part of her time scrubbing floors she could attend to a greater number of patients. Bart's did not follow Guy's example until 1868.

The nurses at Guy's were still without a common dining-room and had to have their meals in the wards or in the corridors. The need for changes in this matter was recognised, but the governors were apparently unwilling to provide the necessary accommodation or to meet the cost of employing sufficient nurses to make an alteration in the system possible. A report on the nursing staff contained the following point of view: "It might reasonably be supposed that the meals could more comfortably be taken at a general table, but, independent of the want of accommodation and organisation for this purpose, its adoption would be attended with much inconvenience, as the duties and exigencies of the wards require a constant supervision."

At the Westminster the nurses had to cook their meals over the fires in the wards. Even as late as 1866 the night superintendent cooked her food at her bedroom fire. This state of affairs was remedied in 1872 when a sub-committee was set up to consider the nurses' conditions of service and the administration of the wards. One of their recommendations was that a room should be set aside as a nurses' dining-room. It was to be furnished with a dining table and twelve Windsor chairs. The sub-committee also agreed to adopt the matron's suggestion that washstands, chests of drawers, cupboards, mirrors and carpets should be provided in the nurses' rooms. Among the other improvements were the provision of distinguishing uniforms for the different grades of nurses, and the purchase of additional chairs for the wards.

The nurses on night duty were to work from 9 p.m. until 10 a.m., while the day nurses commenced duty at 6.30 a.m. and finished at 9 p.m.

Outdoor uniform did not come until much later. In 1897 the nurses at Guy's were given bonnets and cloaks. The main purpose of this step was not to give protection against the weather, but to provide the nurses with a safeguard against being molested by the drunkards and ruffians who frequented the London streets. Even they respected a nurse's uniform.

Other improvements were made in the nurses' conditions of service by giving them pensions and allowing them to take holidays. In 1863 the governors of the London Hospital decided that all nurses who retired after completing twenty years' service should receive a pension not exceeding twelve shillings a week. Two years later they granted the nurses' request to be allowed one week's holiday annually. A pension scheme in which nurses all over the country could participate was started in 1887, when the Royal British Pension Fund for Nurses was inaugurated.

Well before the end of the nineteenth century a new type of nurse appeared in the hospitals. She came from a better-class family than most of her colleagues and was known as a lady-pupil. She paid for her training, and because of her higher standard of education this lasted only twelve months. As was to be expected, it was from the lady pupils that most of the sisters were selected.

In 1895 regulations were laid down for the ward sisters at the Royal Northern Hospital. They were to rise at 6.15 a.m., commence duty at 7 a.m., retire to their rooms at 10 p.m., and extinguish their lights by 10.45 p.m. They had two evenings and two afternoons off duty each week, and a half-day on alternate Saturdays. In addition they had one free day monthly whenever this was practicable, and four weeks' holiday annually.

Although the story of Florence Nightingale has made the sweeping changes in nursing by far the best-known of the reforms in the nineteenth-century hospitals, there were, of course, many other improvements. Yet some aspects of treatment which to us seem matters of plain common sense were very slow in being adopted. Until towards the end of the century medical and surgical cases were still placed in the same wards. Even patients suffering from typhoid fever were mixed with operation cases or fractures. The doctors and nurses were themselves often carriers of infection, for they visited infectious patients and then went immediately to others suffering from non-infectious ailments.

In the operating theatre the old methods still persisted, so that undergoing an operation of any kind continued to be a very dangerous business for the unfortunate patient. The mortality rate in the amputation cases of one of the leading surgeons of the 1870's was about 25 per cent, yet he expressed the opinion that this "may be considered a very satisfactory result."

Lister first advocated the principles of antiseptic surgery in 1865, yet in the eighties some surgeons continued to argue that his methods were ineffective. Unfortunately they could cite many examples to prove their point, for even where antisepsis was practised it was often carried out inefficiently, largely because its principles were improperly understood. There was also opposition from the surgeons because of all the trouble in which antisepsis involved them. No longer were they allowed to operate without washing their hands or their instruments; now hands and instruments had to be soaked in a solution of carbolic acid. The patients' wounds had to be washed with a carbolic lotion, · and the surgeon had to endure the unpleasantness of operating in an atmosphere made damp by a carbolic spray. These precautions seemed to many of the old school to be quite unnecessary, for the deaths from operations continued much as before. They did not realise that the use of all this carbolic was of little avail if they still operated in their old coats, allowed nurses and students to gather round the operating table in their ordinary clothes after having come direct from infectious patients or the post-mortem room, and permitted the patient to be covered with an old blanket which was used for every operation and seldom washed. It was not to be wondered at that mortality among persons operated on in hospitals was much higher than that among those operated on in their own homes. The medical men had an explanation for this high mortality rate; it was due, they said, to the atmosphere of the hospital having become permeated with a poisonous miasma from the many cases of gangrene, blood-poisoning and similar ailments which were always to be found in every hospital.

Because surgery was so often fatal, it was undertaken comparatively rarely, and so an operation was an unusual event, and quite an important one. Preparations for it might begin a week beforehand, when the room to be used (often there was no proper theatre) was carefully scrubbed and fumigated, and the furniture was moved out.

It was not until the beginning of the present century that the antiseptic practices were replaced by the modern principles of asepsis. The aim of aseptic surgery is to sterilise the instruments, the garments of the operators, and everything coming into contact with the patient by means of steam or heat.

The use of anaesthetics preceded the practice of antisepsis. In December, 1846, Robert Liston amputated a man's leg at University College Hospital, London, while the man was anaesthetised with ether. The table on which the operation was performed can still be seen in the College museum. The following year a Scottish physician, James Simpson, discovered the use of chloroform as an anaesthetic. Yet nearly thirty years elapsed before the practice of anaesthetics was regarded as a specialty in its own right. There was no anaesthetist at the Middlesex Hospital until 1874; before that time the other doctors administered chloroform. At St. George's Hospital the assistant apothecary acted as anaesthetist; in 1873 his salary was increased because of his "services in giving chloroform during the last twelve months." In 1879 a "chloroformist" was appointed at a salary of £20 a year.

A later development was the use of X-rays. These were discovered by the German physicist Röntgen in 1895, and the following year the Royal Southern Hospital at Liverpool became the first in this country to have an X-ray apparatus.

Of course, there was usually opposition to the improvements. Some hospitals rejected a few of the innovations outright. The governors of the Royal Northern would not have internal telephones; it is recorded in the minutes that "the Mechanical Telegraph for internal communication was declined, as a bell was considered sufficient." The Royal Northern was not so backward in other respects, though. The staff appear to have been given more consideration than at some other hospitals, for when two of the sisters were taken ill and had to go to the seaside, their expenses were paid. The out-patient arrangements, too, were better than in many other places. In 1869 an investigation into out-patient departments was conducted by *The Lancet* and the report on the Royal Northern, which at that time had more than sixty thousand out-patients annually, was as follows—

The porter frequently refuses admission to persons finely dressed, and those who appear able to contribute something are requested to pay 2/6 to the charity, by doing which they secure the privilege of being examined first. The average receipts from this source are about £1 per week. After the admission of the special cases, the males and females are seen, the porter selecting the feeble and more obviously serious cases for early entrance. The patients are ordered to remain in the waiting rooms; but the ladies are somewhat hard to keep in order, and a threat is posted up that if not obedient the surgeon "will not see one of them." Every patient is examined privately. One only is permitted to remain within a reasonable distance of the consulting-room door, in order to be ready when summoned by a bell. This is as it should be. In the out-patient rooms previously reported on there is no such privacy.

Twenty years later the out-patient arrangements at the Royal Northern were again the subject of comment in the medical press. There were so many out-patients, many with only trivial ailments, that the hospital staff had difficulty in coping with them. The local general practitioners were perturbed, for they feared their livelihoods would suffer; they looked upon the out-patient department as a competitor for their "trade." Fortunately the matter was solved amicably by a joint committee of the hospital medical staff and the general practitioners. They decided that, while first aid must always be given to casualties, applicants for less urgent treatment should be subjected to a means test.

Telephones were not the only new invention to meet with opposition from those who controlled the hospitals. At the Radcliffe Infirmary, Oxford, gas lighting was installed in the corridors in 1851, but not in the wards, because the governors and the staff thought its use there would be harmful to health. For another twenty years the wards continued to be lit by tallow candles. Electric lighting did not come until 1904.

Arrangements for bathing patients still left much to be desired. Until 1874 there were only two fixed baths at the Westminster Hospital and both of these were in the basement. The only other bath provided for the patients was on wheels and had to be shared between all the wards. At the Royal Northern Hospital, founded in 1856, there was no bath until 1860 and this had only cold water, because the committee "felt unable to incur the expense of pipes and stoves."

Gradually improvements were made in the furniture and equipment of all hospitals. In 1885 the old flock mattresses in use at Guy's were replaced by hair mattresses. At the Bristol Royal Infirmary a metal operating table was installed in 1894; previously there had been only an old wooden one. The Royal Southern Hospital, Liverpool, had a washing machine and a sewing machine as early as 1858, and in the same year the Medical Board presented a gymnastic apparatus for use by convalescent patients.

Beer continued to be an important item of hospital dietaries. When the committee of the Worcester Royal Infirmary decided in 1861 that they must economise they were amazed to discover that 6,436 gallons of beer were consumed in twelve months. They ordered that boys under fourteen years of age should be restricted to half a pint a day, whilst child patients less than eight years old should get none at all—they would have to be content with milk! At one children's hospital every child was given a ration of sherry, which was placed on a shelf over his head. Needless to say this presented a great temptation to the nurses and often while a child slept his sherry was removed and tea was put in its place.

When, in 1873, a few people announced that they were going to open a hospital where alcohol would be excluded from the dietary, there was astonishment amongst the medical profession and the general public. Alcohol was regarded as essential for the treatment of all who were sick. But the founders of the Temperance Hospital in Hampstead Road, London, ignored the scorn of a leading medical journal, which exclaimed, "God help the patients!" and the indignation of *The Times*, which expressed gratitude that "there are still coroners and juries whose services could be called in if any lives were lost in the new institution's foolish experiment."

Beer was not the only beverage whose consumption caused concern among hospital authorities. In 1864 one of the members of the Court of Governors of St. Thomas's Hospital drew the attention of his colleagues to the fact that during the past year the patients had drunk 1,336 dozen bottles of soda water and lemonade, while in the same period the patients at Guy's had consumed only 260 dozen. He could not understand this, particularly as there were only 200 beds at St. Thomas's, whereas at Guy's there were three times as many. Furthermore, soda water and lemonade were given only to fever patients and there were not a great many of these. However, the governor did not press the matter when the treasurer explained that the beverages had been ordered by the medical staff, and added, "It would be a bold thing in any governor to dictate to those gentlemen what they should order the patients under their charge."

In many hospitals the most important member of the staff was the house surgeon (a contrast to the position of the person holding this office today, when he is one of the junior members of the medical staff). At Worcester he was known as the Master of the Infirmary. The Committee laid down the administrative duties which he was expected to perform—

He shall take care that the dispenser and the servants properly discharge their respective duties. He shall be responsible for the state of the building and fixtures. He shall each week report to the House Committee the state of the Infirmary. He shall have entire control of the Institution in all matters not directly affecting the honorary medical staff. He shall in case of misconduct on the part of the dispenser or of any servant suspend such person and report to the next meeting of the Executive Committee. He shall provide for the temporary discharge of the duties in the meantime.

The secretary's work was far less onerous. In fact, he was only a clerk, with no administrative duties; all he had to do was collect the subscriptions, keep the minutes and accounts, and send out notices of meetings.

Despite their responsibilities, house surgeons in some hospitals still had to put up with all sorts of restrictions. Perhaps the holder of the office at the Royal Northern was not quite so important as house surgeons elsewhere, for in 1862 "the matter having attracted the attention of one of the Lady Visitors, the Secretary was directed to request the House Surgeon to desist from smoking at unsuitable hours in the sitting-room on the ground floor of the Establishment."

The rules governing the behaviour of the medical students were still very strict. At the Manchester Royal Infirmary they were not allowed to associate with the nurses, and one of them was forbidden to enter the Infirmary for three months because he "induced two nurses to go with him to a place of amusement."

The recognition of nursing as a profession for young ladies from better-class families was followed by the recruitment of educated young women for other work in hospitals. During the eighties it was decided to employ them as clinical clerks at the Hospital for Sick Children in Great Ormond Street, London. Early in the following decade the House of Lords appointed a Select Committee to investigate the over-crowding of out-patient departments in the London hospitals. It was suggested to them that each hospital should have a trained social worker who could determine the needs of those who applied for free treatment. This proposal led to the appointment of lady almoners, and so another profession in the hospital service was opened to women.

New wards to provide more beds, new equipment, and increasing numbers of patients meant, of course, that more money was needed. Subscriptions, donations and legacies did not provide sufficient income, and all sorts of devices were used to raise funds —whist drives, carnivals, flag days and concerts. Those who could not afford cash were asked to contribute in kind during egg weeks, potato weeks and vegetable weeks.

Two other innovations which helped considerably in augmenting the income were the Hospital Sunday Fund and the Hospital Saturday Fund. The former was a collection made in places of worship on a certain Sunday in each year. The Saturday Fund was similar, except that the collection was made amongst the workers in factories instead of from the congregations in churches.

The year of Queen Victoria's Diamond Jubilee, 1897, saw the beginning of a very important fund, which for more than sixty years has supplied not only financial aid but many other forms of assistance to hospitals and convalescent homes in and around London. It was originally known as "The Prince of Wales's Hospital Fund for London to Commemorate the Sixtieth Year of the Queen's Reign," but in 1902 its title was changed to "King Edward's Hospital Fund for London." Its aim was to obtain "at least £100,000 additional revenue for the Metropolitan hospitals and convalescent institutions." In the first year nearly a quarter of a million pounds were raised and this money was used to assist ninety-five hospitals, which between them had almost seven hundred beds closed because of lack of funds.

Until the middle of the nineteenth century nearly all the hospitals were in the larger towns, and consequently people living in rural areas who were taken ill or met with accidents often had to be taken long distances to hospital or else remain in their own homes, where there were no facilities for treatment. This led to much additional suffering and loss of life. The first step to remedy this state of affairs was taken at the village of Cranleigh in Surrey in 1859, when a local surgeon, Mr. Albert Napper, opened the first cottage hospital. It was in a former vicarage and had only four beds. Thirty-five years later there were over six hundred cottage hospitals in Britain. They proved a great boon not only to sick countryfolk but also to the local general practitioners, whose status was raised considerably by their being able to perform fairly serious operations and treat their patients after they were admitted to hospital.

CHAPTER VIII

TOWARDS A NATIONAL HEALTH SERVICE

By the end of the nineteenth century England had many hundreds of hospitals. Yet there were still areas where the hospital accommodation was far below the needs of the population, while other districts had a superfluity of hospital beds. Plenty of people had helped to provide the hospitals; nobody had attempted to organise them into any sort of system.

The hospitals fell into two main groups: (a) the voluntary hospitals; and (b) the local authority hospitals. The first group were all those whose history has been mentioned in this book, together with many more founded and maintained in a similar manner, by the voluntary efforts of the people. Most of the hospitals in the second group were Poor Law infirmaries; there were also a fair number of hospitals established by local authorities as a result of legislation passed during the nineteenth century in an attempt to cope with various infectious and epidemic diseases. Many of the voluntary hospitals were in need of funds; local authorities were often cheeseparing with the amounts they were prepared to pay from the rates towards the maintenance and improvement of their hospitals.

It was becoming increasingly obvious to some of the more far-seeing people concerned with hospitals that the government would have to intervene in this branch of public welfare to a far greater extent than in the past. If it did not provide financial aid, many of the hospitals might have to close. It was not only money that the government would have to find; they would also have to organise the hospitals into a proper system, to ensure that the best possible use was made of the money and that the people throughout the country had adequate hospital facilities within a reasonable distance of their homes. The hospital history of the first four and a half decades of this century is mainly an account of the attempts

of various governments and other bodies to find satisfactory
solutions to these problems. These efforts are briefly summarised
later in this chapter.

But before turning to politics it is worth while learning something of hospital life in 1914, shortly after the outbreak of the
First World War. How it appeared to one who found herself
rather unexpectedly a nurse has been well described by Lady
Diana Cooper in her autobiography[1]—

Guy's looked very Dickensian that afternoon beneath its dark
drizzle. A few shivering nurses in cotton dresses were being blown
about the wide courtyard and open arcaded passages. We rang the
bell at a side entrance. The door was opened by an old housekeeper
in black with a hospital cap. She was as dry and grey as cinders. She
led us to an upper bedroom giving on to the courtyard. Here I
unpacked my modest little trunk—some underclothes, some books,
concealed cosmetics, clock, pencils and paper, and pampering hot-
water-bottle. Every movement was watched by the old house-
Gestapo. Then they dressed me. My mother writhed. I felt myself
more a nun leaving the world than a V.A.D. probationer. There was
no long glass, but I later saw what was making my mother so
appalled, for indeed I did look horrible. The dress was just off the
floor and gathered at the back only. The print was of a minute and
colourless mauve-and-white pin-stripe. The apron was cut to deform
the figure. The stiff collar, cuffs and belt gleaming with starch gave
cleanth and trimness. The absurd cap attached to the tip-top of the
head by an unreliable pin protected one's hair neither from lice nor
from contagious germs. There were the universal black stockings
and flat black shoes. I was led away from my mother who was left
disconsolate. I could not feel myself naughty, only perhaps heartless.

They took me to a women's surgical ward called Charity. There
I was passed on to Sister Charity, a very comely, shy young Sister
in well-fitted becoming blue, with a cap held on by fresh white
strings and a pleated bow. No smiles. A training hospital in 1914 was
as inhuman as the army. No speaking to superiors before being
spoken to. All these rules had to be learnt by trial and error, as I
found out when next day I said "Good morning" to Matron. One
could be schoolgirlish with the probationers though not with the
Head Nurse (still unqualified), whose cap was tied on and was
therefore unofficially referred to as "Strings" . . .

[1] *The Rainbow Comes and Goes* by Lady Diana Cooper (Rupert Hart-Davis).
Quoted by permission of the author and publishers.

... It was a fine old L-shaped ward with deep embrasured windows on both sides. It held between twenty and thirty beds with a few children's cots scattered around. It had an atmosphere of brightness and even happiness—a big fire in the grate, the convalescents sitting round it, the pretty Sister and a pleasant bustle. I left it after Sister had said prayers at eight o'clock, had some supper and went to my austere little room.

Then the next morning—

A biting wind blew us into the beautiful old chapel, where for a quarter of an hour we prayed to be given strength and patience with the patients and for the safety of an ever-lengthening list of Guy's nurses abroad with the Forces.

From chapel we filed over to a modern building where our very nasty breakfast was waiting for us—tea limitless, off-white "standard" bread, marge (in those days uneatable), tinned eggs (then a novelty and considered poisonous), good sausages or stalish fish. My trouble was wanting not to eat, as I was both vain and rather fat, yet knowing that a high-graded Sister on a little rostrum was eagle-eyeing each nurse who was late, who was ill-dressed or who appeared fastidious. Often in later days I would be called with several other miscreants after the meal and reproved severely. Did I not know that nurses were different from other people? Their lives were dedicated to the sick, maybe dying, and they must keep up their strength by sensible diet in order not to be found wanting. . . .

At ten o'clock a cup of tea was snatched by half the nurses in the little kitchen attached to the ward. There the ward-maid operated. She was never off her knees except to put the kettle on—she was called Polly—and to heat up the excellent food the patients were given—good meat, chicken, creamy rice-pudding, fresh fruit compôtes. Soon after this break the doctors would arrive, followed by a knot of students. Matron had already passed through the ward, met and escorted by Sister, silent and inscrutable. She spoke neither to the patients nor to the nurses. She was formidable. To be sent for by Matron (if a probationer) meant tears before, during and after the interview. . . .

Very soon it was 11.15, at which unexpected hour one shift of nurses went to dinner. The second shift went at twelve and returned at one, and took over the ward with an interval for tea till eight p.m., while the first shift was out from two till six and remained on duty till nine. Dinner was very nasty, but one could wolf it and regain one's room, put one's aching feet up on the bed and read the papers and one's letters. Feet hurt more when one got up. Back in the ward by twelve to serve dinners. This was done ceremoniously by Sister, extra-aproned like a chef, sharpening her carvers on a stone and dispensing to her understrappers plates of different robustness and lightness—"Mrs. 10 and little B's [cot]," "That's not enough for 22, add some more sprouts."

At one o'clock bed-making, general tidying up, preparing for operations and visitors. And at two, my first day out and away, in a bonnet not unlike the Salvation Army but less becoming, and a long tubular narrow cape to the ankles—no arm-movement possible. We looked like caterpillars. Later I would dress in plain clothes for outings, but on my first day there was no question of not showing myself to be a nurse *par excellence*. I got back to Arlington Street by bus before they had finished their 1.45 luncheon. Eagerly awaiting me (I was by then the Pride of the Family) they bombarded me with questions and I gave, probably, an exaggeratedly dramatic account of hospital life with no details omitted or extenuated. I rested and was petted and tucked into a fine tea. The hospital provided tea, but I think no nurse whose off-afternoon it was took advantage of the Indian stew and rock-bottom cakes.

In the ward at six, more washing, four-hourly fomentations, tonics and bedpans, temperatures, pulses, respiration charts, convalescents, prayers and hand-over to the "night people." There was a traditional dislike and distrust of the "night people." The most popular nurse, when her turn came for night duty, became one of these heartless, negligent, half-asleep murderesses who let No. 15 "go," i.e. die. Deaths are rarer in hospitals than laymen imagine, especially in a surgical ward. Accident and medical wards have more. But death in Charity came in a blue moon. I do not know if it is true that the small hours take the biggest toll of mortals, but the dying certainly did tend to flicker out at dawn, and it was always the fault of the night people, particularly in the eyes of that poor creature's day nurse. For we each had our own patients. I don't think that is so today, so all the pride in one another is lost. . . .

I enjoyed the months at Guy's. V.A.D.s (it was the first month of their infancy and there were but two of us) were very well received. We dressed the same as the staff and were treated in exactly the same way. I was allowed to do everything the upper nurses were allowed, except dispensing, but in a few weeks I was giving injections, intravenous and saline, preparing for operations, cutting abscesses and once even saying prayers in Sister's absence. In some respects I had an easier time than the first- and second-year probationers and more variety of work, as my rank changed with whatever nurse was off-duty. There was no sweating at classes with examinations looming ahead. I could go to the lectures, but I was not eligible to enter for the examination. The first year took a lot of probationers off the list. The life was excessively hard if you were not very strong. Their feet and mine suffered intolerably. We were not allowed to sit down during working hours, so that it meant (meals excluded) eight solid hours on one's feet, and a ninth hour walking the hospital.

One could steal a minute or two in the kitchen, where there was a chair, also a cupboard of left-overs, cold creamy rice-pudding, cold chicken perhaps.

Finding was eating. . . .

To be discovered going out with a student could mean dismissal in your third and last year. Punishments were severe. Twice late for closing-time at ten p.m. would forfeit your long-desired week-end, and less serious misdemeanours would stop your rare theatre-leave. . . .

I got on very well and was popular with my fellow-nurses and I think with the patients. Nurses took it in turn to bring a cake for two o'clock teas and there were "dormy feasts" in Matron's house with hot blackberry tisane, delicatessen, sweets, cigarettes, suppressed songs and laughter, the larks that I had missed by never being a schoolgirl.

During the course of the war accommodation for the sick and wounded was provided in buildings never intended for use as hospitals. In August, 1914, there were about 7,000 beds in military hospitals; by the end of the war there were over 360,000. Many of these were in schools, colleges, Poor Law institutions and mental asylums, or in hutted hospitals. A large number of hospitals were established by voluntary organisations and private individuals. All offers of help for the sick and wounded had to be made to the Joint War Committee of the British Red Cross Society and Order of St. John, and they accepted over one thousand hospitals, ranging in size from six to two hundred or more beds.

After the First World War the Minister of Health appointed a committee under the chairmanship of the late Viscount Cave "to consider the present financial position of the voluntary hospitals, and to make recommendations as to any action which should be taken to assist them." The committee received reports on their finances from 672 hospitals, and 378 of these were in debt to a total of over £1,000,000. The committee recommended that a hospitals commission should be set up, and this in its turn should establish voluntary hospital committees covering the whole country. One of the commission's chief duties would be to spend £1,000,000, which Parliament should be asked to sanction as a temporary grant. It should also have power to recommend other grants, subject to similar contributions being forthcoming from private sources.

The government set up the Voluntary Hospitals Commission in 1921, but gave it only £500,000 to spend instead of £1,000,000. Nearly half the sum was allocated to the London hospitals. England was divided into forty-six areas and voluntary hospital committees were established in thirty-seven of these. They were given various duties to perform, such as encouraging co-operation between hospitals, organising contributory schemes, and investigating the hospital needs of their areas.

The Local Government Act of 1929 gave local authorities wider powers to provide hospitals. It encouraged them to co-operate with voluntary hospital committees; in fact, it required them, when dealing with the provision of hospital accommodation, to consult "such committee or other body as they consider to represent both the governing bodies and the medical and surgical staffs of the voluntary hospitals." This led voluntary hospitals in some parts of the country to set up bodies to represent them and the medical and surgical staffs. In the Metropolis the London Voluntary Hospitals Committee was established to co-operate with the London County Council, and similar bodies were set up in other large cities, but in the country as a whole the effort was half-hearted. Only eighty-three committees were set up in the 146 local authority areas, and thirty-four of these never held a single meeting! Despite this, the Act was a great step forward. The functions of the old boards of guardians, who had administered the Poor Law infirmaries, were transferred to the local authorities and the stigma of pauperism was removed from admission to the infirmaries. The encouragement which the Act gave to local authorities to extend their hospitals led to great improvements in many areas.

Six years later a commission was set up under the chairmanship of Viscount Sankey to inquire into the position of the voluntary hospitals and make recommendations on the measures to be taken to develop their policy and safeguard their future. The commission recommended that the country should be divided into hospital regions, each with a council to correlate its hospital work and needs. The work of the regional councils should be co-ordinated by a central council. In each region the hospitals should be grouped round a central hospital, and regional funds created for the benefit of all the hospitals, which would also be aided financially by the government and by local authorities. Various improvements were recommended for nursing and administrative staffs; nurses should receive higher pay; there should be a higher educational standard for entrants to the nursing profession; matrons should be regarded as administrative officers and have direct access to committees; the special qualifications required for chief administrative officers of hospitals should be recognised; there should be a system of education in hospital administration; and all nursing and administrative staff should participate in a pension scheme.

The Sankey Report was issued in 1937; in the same year Political and Economic Planning published a survey of *The British Health Services,* based on the work of two hundred investigators. This drew attention to the large number of different agencies which had "come into being as a kind of patchy improvisation without regard to any general scheme, and bringing in its train overlapping, competition, S.O.S.s for funds, and other evils, with the result that the public is bewildered in a maze of services, each working independently of the other." A view expressed by the Royal Commission on Local Government in the Tyneside area was repeated: "The most efficient and economical way to administer the medical and allied services, including hospitals, is by a single regional authority covering a wide area."

In 1938 the British Medical Association published *A General Medical Service for the Nation* (a revision of a document issued in 1930) and *A Statement on Hospital Policy*. The B.M.A. wanted a planned national health policy closely co-ordinating the various sections of the medical service, and they too favoured a hospital service on a regional basis.

In the same year the Ministry of Health took the first practical step towards organising hospital regions when they established the Emergency Medical Services. This move was made because of the threat of war. Three hundred thousand beds had to be found for the civilian casualties expected if London and other large centres of population were bombed. England and Wales were divided into twelve regions, each with a senior hospital officer and consultant advisers. Co-operation on a regional basis between voluntary and municipal hospitals was one of the aims of the Nuffield Provincial Hospitals Trust, which was established in 1940, and in less than twelve months ten joint hospital councils had been set up.

A further move was made by the British Medical Association in 1940, when they set up a Medical Planning Commission "to study war-time developments and their effects on the country's medical services both present and future." The Commission's seventy-three members were representative of a very wide range of interests. A draft interim report was issued in 1942; no final report ever appeared. The Commission stressed the need for a unified hospital system organised on a regional basis.

As part of the preparations in connection with the establishment of the Emergency Medical Services—or E.M.S., as they came to be known—the Government had in the early months of 1938 carried out a comprehensive survey of the country's hospital accommodation. This showed that there were about 403,000 beds; of these, 103,000 were usually vacant. By discharging patients, placing beds in rooms not normally used as wards, and converting buildings near hospitals into accommodation for casualties, it was planned to increase the number of vacant beds to 627,000 within seven days of the outbreak of war. It was anticipated that any war would commence with a large-scale aerial bombardment; by the end of the first fortnight over 300,000 beds would be required for casualties. The "phoney war" had not been foreseen: in the first eight months of the war there were less than one thousand civilian casualties and only about four thousand from the Services. Consequently there were thousands of vacant beds, and not unnaturally there was some resentment among civilians who were in need of treatment but were told that they could not be admitted to hospital because beds had to be reserved for war wounded.

Not until the evacuation of the British Expeditionary Force from France at the end of May, 1940, was there any large number of casualties. Then just over thirty thousand wounded from the Services were admitted to hospitals in various parts of the country. At the same time the Battle of Britain commenced, with air raids mainly on London, the ports and the industrial towns. During the next twelve months nearly fifty thousand people were seriously injured during these attacks, but even this figure was far below the number which hospital staffs had been led to expect.

Nevertheless, their work must not be minimised. Despite depletion by the call-up for the Forces, they coped magnificently during the dark nights of bombardment. Many of the hospital buildings suffered considerable damage, some being put completely out of action for a time. So that emergency operations could be carried out during the blitz, operating theatres were set up in basements. Nearly all the large hospitals in London had to reduce their numbers of beds because of bomb damage; St. Thomas's received six direct hits.

The air raids continued for four years, although not on such a large scale as during the Battle of Britain. There was, however, a great increase in the number of Service casualties. In 1942 there were over 220,000 and in 1943 nearly 270,000. The air raids were followed in the summer of 1944 by the flying bombs, launched from the French coast. Between the middle of June and the end of July there were over fifty thousand casualties, mostly in the

London region. Again there was serious damage to hospitals. St. Mary Abbots Hospital at Kensington, with over eight hundred beds, had to be evacuated and closed after a flying bomb had hit it, killing five members of the staff and thirteen patients. By the end of October over one hundred hospitals had been damaged.

The attacks continued for nine months, and after they ceased there was a lull of only about six months before the Germans tried another means of causing death and destruction. This was the long-range rocket or V.2, as it was commonly known. Again the great majority of the casualties were in the London area— over four thousand in four months. There was, of course, further damage to hospitals: in London nearly a thousand beds were put out of use.

While the conflict raged the Government had announced their policy for hospitals after the war. It was intended to set up a comprehensive hospital service to ensure that "appropriate treatment shall be readily available to every person in need of it." Action to establish this comprehensive service was not delayed until the end of the war. There were discussions with all the interested parties, and in 1944 a White Paper entitled *A National Health Service* was issued. This set out a plan to enable the nation "to obtain medical advice and treatment of every kind without charge." This plan was not meant to be a firm proposal; the Government's purpose was to stimulate discussion, and they aimed to do this by placing before the people their idea of the best organisation for a National Health Service.

They proposed to base the Service on the existing local government system. The municipal hospitals in each area would be administered by a Joint Board representing the county councils and county borough councils in the area. The voluntary hospitals would have to continue to find a large amount of the funds they required, in order to avoid "the end of the voluntary movement." They would not be administered by the Joint Boards, but would be invited to take part in the area plans.

For the next fourteen or fifteen months there were discussions about the White Paper and various alternative suggestions were put forward. Then in the summer of 1945 there was a general election and the new Government announced that they would not be bound by the discussions which had taken place and would go back to the beginning—to the White Paper. In March, 1946, they placed a Bill before the House of Commons which differed greatly from the Coalition Government's White Paper, particularly in so far as hospitals were concerned. The municipal hospitals were to be taken away from the local authorities and they and the voluntary hospitals were to be transferred to State ownership. They would be grouped into large areas, each of which would be administered by a Regional Hospital Board, responsible for the overall planning of the hospital service in the region. The regions would be divided into smaller areas and the day-to-day administration of the hospitals in these areas would be carried out by Hospital Management Committees.

This was the plan which was finally adopted, for the Bill was passed by both Houses of Parliament and received the Royal Assent in November, 1946. Nearly two years were allowed for all the administrative preparations that were necessary, and thus, on 5th July, 1948, the National Health Service came into being and nearly all of the hospitals in the country became for the first time part of the same system.

CHAPTER IX

THE SICK IN MIND

THIS history would not be complete if it did not include the story of the hospitals where the mentally afflicted receive treatment. These hospitals have not so far been mentioned because for centuries they have been a class quite distinct from the others. They were, in fact, the first specialist hospitals, except, of course, for the lazar-houses.

In the early Middle Ages the insane were admitted to the same hospitals as people who were diseased in body. They were not even accommodated in different wards. When it was first decided to separate them is not known, but the first hospital to become famous as a refuge for the insane was the Bethlem Hospital at Bishopsgate, London.

This is probably the oldest asylum in the world with a continuous history. It was founded as a priory in 1247, but the first record of insane persons being accommodated there is dated 1403. For the previous fifteen years the master of the hospital had been one of the king's chaplains, but he had cared nothing for the well-being of the patients and had not visited the establishment. He had made a legal agreement with Peter Taverner, the hospital janitor, assigning to him the "safe keeping of the poor and sick as well as the custody of the alms." Peter's scandalous behaviour led Henry IV to order two of his chaplains to conduct an investigation into his conduct, and when their report appeared in 1403 thirty-five articles of indictment were laid against him. One of the crimes with which he was charged was the theft of certain articles belonging to the hospital, including two pairs of stocks, four pairs of iron manacles, six iron chains with locks and five other iron chains. Such objects as these were obviously used for restraining lunatics, and there is confirmation of the fact that insane people were maintained at the hospital in the evidence given by a woman witness at Peter's trial. She said that eighteen months previously her neighbours had put her into the hospital to recover her reason. Peter was found guilty and dismissed from his post.

The "treatment"—if such it could be called—of lunatics by placing them in chains was the normal practice in the Middle Ages and for centuries to come. In fact, restraint and cruelty were often the only forms of treatment they received. In the seventeenth century a prominent physician said: "Nothing is more necessary and more effective for the recovery of these people than forcing them to respect and fear intimidation. By this method the mind, held back by restraint, is induced to give up its arrogance and wild ideas and soon becomes meek and orderly. This is why maniacs often recover much sooner if they are treated with torture and treatment in hovels instead of with medicaments."

Bethlem—or Bedlam as it was familiarly called—was not London's only asylum during the Middle Ages; insane people were also kept at an establishment in St. Martin's Lane. Stow, writing of this area in his *Survey of London*, which was published in 1598, said: "Then had ye an house, wherein some time were distraught and lunatike people, of what antiquity founded, or by whom, I have not read, neither of the suppression; but it was said that some time a king of England, not liking such a kind of people to remaine so neare his pallace, caused them to be removed further off to Bethlem without Bishopsgate of London, and to that Hospitall the said house by Charing Cross doth yet remaine." This story was confirmed in 1632 by commissioners appointed to inquire into scandals at Bethlem Hospital. In their report they stated: "Only we find by an ancient lease made in the reign of Henry VII that in the place where these houses now stand was anciently an old house with gardens and grounds thereunto belonging called the Stone House, which Stone House we do likewise find in a bill preferred to the Exchequer in December of 9 James I by Agnes Garland that it was sometimes employed for the harbouring of mad and distracted persons, before such time as they were removed to the present hospital of Bethlem, without Bishopsgate."

Another medieval asylum was at Barking in Essex. It was founded by a priest about 1370 "for the sustentation of poor priests and other men and women that were sicke of the phrenzie, there to remaine till they were perfectly whole and restored to good memorie."

Less than forty years after the dismissal of Peter Taverner another inquiry was ordered into "various scandals and abuses at the hospital of St. Mary of Beddeleem, due to the neglect of former masters." It was alleged that "alms-giving and other accustomed works of piety, such as the succour of distraught lunatics and of other poor and sickly persons, who flock to the hospital daily, and there reside, are like to be abolished, unless a remedy is speedily applied." Apparently a remedy was found, for in 1451 William Gregory, the Mayor of London, wrote: "A church of Our Lady that is named Bedlam. And in that place are found many men that have fallen out of their wits. Right well are they cared for in that place, and some are restored to health again, but some are there forever, for they are incurable."

As was the case with many other hospitals, the dissolution of the monasteries brought about the suppression of Bethlem, but in 1546, in response to an appeal from the Lord Mayor, Henry VIII granted it to the City and it was refounded as one of the royal hospitals. At first it was administered by the court of aldermen through a "keeper," who had to submit his accounts to the city chamberlain, but in 1556 it was placed under the control of the governors of Christ's Hospital. This arrangement was short-lived, however, for in the following year the governors of Bridewell were made responsible for its administration. They appointed three "surveyors of Bethlem" to look after the day-to-day affairs of the hospital. In order to raise funds the surveyors sent a proctor to Cambridge, Ely and Lincoln to beg for money; in addition, a royal decree was issued ordering collections on behalf of the hospital to be made in every church in the country.

The keeper was allowed to take private patients, provided that he also accepted any patients sent by Bridewell. At first he received no payment for the Bridewell patients, but later he was

paid sixpence or sevenpence a week for each of them. From a
report of a governors' inspection made in 1598 it appears that
there were at that time only twenty patients. Six of these were
from Bridewell and the remainder were private patients. The
payment which the keeper received for the latter varied from
1s. 4d. to five shillings a week. Among them were a Dutchman,
a Spaniard and a woman who had been an inmate for twenty-five
years. There were no women attendants, but if a female patient
was pregnant she was attended by the porter's wife. The only fire
in the whole of the hospital was in the kitchen, and the governors
found that conditions throughout the hospital were quite unsatisfactory. "We do find," they said, "other defaults in the said
house in such sort that it is not fit for any man to dwell in, in
which it was left by the keeper, for that it was so loathsomely and
filthily kept that it was not fit for any man to come into the said
house."

The last man to hold the appointment of keeper was Dr.
Hilkiah Crooke, who was dismissed in 1633; he had visited the
hospital only on quarter-days and most of the funds had gone into
his own pocket. Two of the governors carried out a surprise
inspection in 1631 and found that sometimes the patients had to
exist for days on a few scraps, and on the Sunday preceding the
inspection all they had had to eat was four pounds of cheese,
which had to be shared between thirty of them!

After Dr. Crooke's dismissal the steward became the chief
administrative officer. There seems to have been little immediate
improvement, however, for the first steward also had to be dismissed. He had been stealing the provisions and falsifying the
accounts.

Up to the middle of the seventeenth century the governors do
not appear to have concerned themselves a great deal with the
welfare of the patients, but from the records of their activities
during the second half of the century it appears that this received
a little more attention. In 1655 they ordered "that no officer or
servant shall give any blows or ill language to any of the mad
folks on pain of losing his place." The governors themselves were

"entreated to go as often as possible to see how the lunatics are used and how officers and servants behave themselves." They also decided to consider "how best the men and women may be lodged and kept asunder." At this time, according to one writer, "the men and women were huddled together in the same ward." John Evelyn visited the hospital in 1657 and recorded the event in his diary: "I stepped into Bedlam, where I saw several poor miserable creatures in chains; one of them was mad with making verses." In 1662 it was decided that the female patients should be kept in a separate ward, and a matron was appointed to take charge of them.

In 1674 the governors came to the conclusion that the building was in such a ruinous condition that a new hospital would have to be built; furthermore, it was far too small for the number of people requiring admission. A site was found at Moorfields and a magnificent structure costing £17,000 was erected and opened in 1676. The site was given by the City Corporation and the cost of the building was met partly from donations and partly by loans. There was accommodation for 150 patients; the men were in cells on the lower gallery and the women in cells on the upper gallery. Sometimes a few of the well-behaved patients were allowed to leave their cells and go into the galleries, but normally only visitors were permitted in these.

These visitors—members of the general public—were admitted on payment of a penny, and the entrances they used were known as the penny gates. Thousands of people used to take advantage of this practice each year and the lunatics of Bedlam were, in fact, regarded as one of the sights of London. One physician actually expressed the opinion that company was very beneficial to the patients, and a writer stated: "I saw a hundred spectators making sport of the miserable inhabitants, provoking them into furies of rage." Clergy and others made vain protests, and it was not until 1770 that it was ruled that visitors must in future be admitted by ticket only, and must be accompanied by attendants.

By this time Bethlem had ceased to be the only public asylum for the insane. Some accommodation was provided for them at

St. Peter's Hospital in Bristol, which was founded in 1696, and a lunatic ward was established at Guy's Hospital in 1728. The first new hospital intended solely for the insane was the Bethel Hospital at Norwich, which was opened in 1713, while in 1751 St. Luke's Hospital in London was erected by voluntary subscriptions.

It seems that the abuses at Bethlem were one of the things that led to the foundation of St. Luke's. In June, 1750, six men, including a doctor, a druggist, an apothecary and two merchants, met at a London tavern to discuss the possibility of founding a hospital for poor lunatics. They decided to issue a statement pointing out that Bethlem Hospital was incapable of receiving a great number of the insane who applied for admission there, and proposing that it would be "a most useful and necessary charity to establish an Hospital where such unhappy persons may be immediately admitted, and have the proper means of cure early administered to them."

A subscription list was opened, and a second meeting was held about a fortnight later, at which it was stated that six London apothecaries had undertaken to supply all the drugs and medicines required at the hospital during the first three years of its existence free of charge. Donations rolled in, a committee was formed, and the search for a suitable building commenced. By October the committee were able to approach the City of London for the lease of a building at Moorfields, which they proposed to adapt as their hospital. The lease was granted, the alterations commenced and in July, 1751, little more than twelve months after the project was first mooted, patients were admitted to St. Luke's Hospital—a name given to it because it was in the parish of St. Luke. By January, 1752, there was accommodation for twenty-six patients and three resident staff.

Little is known of the appearance of either the exterior or the interior of this hospital, but it certainly does not seem to have been an attractive place. One writer described it as "a neat but very plain edifice . . . a building of considerable length, plastered over and whitened, with ranges of small square windows on which no decorations have been bestowed." The patients lived in small rooms known as cells. For a few years they all had to share the same common room, but in 1754 another room was provided. One unpleasant feature of the hospital was a large cold plunge bath, which was constructed in 1752 at a cost of £13. It was thought that some shock, such as being thrown suddenly into a cold bath, would shake lunatics out of their moods of insanity. One medical officer expressed the opinion that immersion was "valuable in certain cases and with proper precautions," and a bath continued to be used at St. Luke's until 1856. It seems a little surprising that the practice should have ceased even then, for the last patient to be ducked declared that he was cured by his immersion!

A special sub-committee drew up a lengthy list of regulations governing the administration of the hospital. These aimed at preventing some of the abuses which were a feature of Bethlem. The patients were not to be exposed to public view; the messenger had to report to the keeper if any stranger wished to come into the hospital; any servant who accepted a reward of any kind from a patient or a friend of a patient was to be dismissed; the hospital was to be cleaned daily before 10 a.m.; and the physician and surgeon were to visit it at least twice a week. Before a patient could be admitted a very detailed procedure had to be observed. A person applying for the admission of a patient had to complete two certificates; one of these had to be signed by the minister and church-wardens or overseer of the poor of the parish and the other by a doctor. Then the person who had witnessed these signatures had to make an oath in the presence of a justice of the peace. The certificates were then signed by the governor of the hospital and submitted, with a petition, to the secretary. Even then the person applying for the patient's admission had not completed all the formalities. He had to attend the next meeting of the House Committee and also find two householders who were willing to enter into a bond of £100 to remove the patient when he was discharged.

At first persons who had suffered from insanity for more than a year or who had been discharged as uncured from any other mental institution were not admitted. Later this rule was relaxed and uncured patients were admitted providing a fee of five shillings a week was paid.

The first physician of the hospital was Dr. William Battie, whose ideas on the treatment of insanity were regarded as being far in advance of his time. Even so, he thought that some restraint was useful, and in 1750 the committee authorised the purchase of twelve pairs of handcuffs and twelve leg logs. His ideas on food also cannot be considered advanced, for he was of the opinion that veal was unnecessary and that pork was improper for the patients, and it appears that they had a monotonous diet of bread, oatmeal, butter, cheese, beef and mutton, although the amounts of these foodstuffs which they received were certainly adequate.

In the first twelve months the number of patients more than doubled, reaching fifty-seven in February, 1753. The decision in 1754 to admit incurable patients led to a further increase, and from then until 1761 there were about twenty incurable patients and fifty others. During the first ten years 749 patients were admitted and 363 of these were discharged as cured.

At first the staff consisted of two head keepers (husband and wife) and two male and two female attendants. The head keepers were paid a joint salary of £30 a year, while the annual wages of the male attendants were £10 and those of the female attendants were £8. In addition they received free board and lodging and also certain gratuities.

In 1787 the hospital was transferred to a splendid new building in Old Street. The move was chiefly brought about by the governors' desire to assist a larger number of poor lunatics, and the erection of a new hospital was made possible by a bequest of £30,000. Following the opening of the new building the number of patients increased rapidly, and by 1792 there were 228.

Although the hospital looked fine from the outside, it was not nearly so pleasant inside. In each of the single bedrooms there was only a small window consisting of four panes. The wards had no heating of any kind, and the only furniture consisted of tables and forms. The patients had to sleep on loose straw which was placed on wooden bedsteads, and the incurable patients did not even have bedsteads, but only straw. Yet St. Luke's was regarded as one of the best hospitals of its kind in the whole of Europe.

So far mention has been made only of the public hospitals for the insane, but a large number of the mentally afflicted were maintained in private madhouses. Some of these were quite large, with several hundred patients; others were very small, having only two or three inmates. Their proprietors claimed that their methods were very successful, but many of them desired only to increase their incomes and cared little about the patients, who were often kept in terrible conditions.

The following advertisement was issued by the owner of a madhouse in Clerkenwell—

> In Clerkenwell Close, where the figures of Mad People are over the Gate, liveth one who by the blessing of God cures all Lunatick, distracted or mad people; he seldom exceeds three months in the cure of the Maddest Person that comes in his house; several have been cured in a fortnight and some in less time; he has cured several from Bedlam, and other madhouses in and about the city, and has conveniency for people of what quality soever. No cure—No money.

The proprietor of this madhouse did not reveal how he brought about these remarkable cures, but Dr. Fallowes, who had an asylum in Lambeth, gave details of his methods in a book which he published in 1705. He explained the cause of insanity by stating that a mad person's brain

> is disturbed by black vapours which clog the finer vessels through which the animal spirits ought freely to pass, and the whole mass of blood, being disordered, either overloads the small veins of the brain, or by too quick a motion, causes a hurry and confusion of the mind, from which ensues a giddiness and at length a fury.

His cure for this "fury" was a substance which he said he had discovered and which he called the Incomparable Oleum Cephalicum. He described it thus—

> It is of an excellent and pleasant smell, and by raising small pustules upon the head, which I always anoint with it, opens the

parts which are condensed and made almost insensible by the black vapours fixed upon the brain; it confirms its texture, strengthens the vessels, and gives a freedom to the blood and spirit enclosing them.

Dr. Fallowes claimed that he had received £10 a quart for this remarkable oil, but he felt such compassion for the poor that he was willing to accept only £4!

Little attention was paid to the terrible conditions in many of the private madhouses until 1763, when the House of Commons appointed a Select Committee to inquire into them. Three factors were largely responsible for the agitation which led to the setting up of this committee. Two of them were cases concerning applications for writs of habeas corpus in respect of inmates of madhouses; the other was an article in the *Gentleman's Magazine*. In 1761 a court ruling was obtained enabling a doctor, her attorney and her nearest blood relation to have access to Mrs. Deborah D'Vebre, whose husband had sent her to a private madhouse in Chelsea. The doctor soon decided that the woman was not mad, and, moreover, he suspected that she had never been insane. An affidavit from him was read in court, and as a result she was set free. In the following year a similar attempt to obtain a writ of habeas corpus in respect of a mental patient failed because a doctor stated that the woman concerned was definitely insane. Then in 1763 the *Gentleman's Magazine* drew attention to the fact that people who were quite sane were frequently lodged in these madhouses by relatives who wanted them out of the way. A man sent his wife to a private asylum because she was extravagant, and several girls were placed in the same madhouse by their friends in order to break off love affairs of which they disapproved. The article gave some idea of the treatment meted out to these unfortunate people—

When a person is forcibly taken or artfully decoyed into a private madhouse he is, without any authority or any further charge than that of an impatient heir, a mercenary relation, or a pretended friend, instantly seized upon by a set of inhuman ruffians trained up to this barbarous profession, stripped naked, and conveyed to a dark room. If the patient complains, the attendant brutishly orders him not to rave, calls for assistants, and ties him down to a bed, from which he is not released until he submits to their pleasure. Next morning, a doctor is gravely introduced who, taking the report of the keeper, pronounces the unfortunate person a lunatic, and declares that he must be reduced by physic. If the revolted victim offers to argue against it by alleging any proofs of sanity, a motion is made by the waiter for the doctor to withdraw, and if the patient, or rather the prisoner, persists in vindicating his reason, or refuses to take the dose, he is then deemed raving mad; the banditti of the whole house are called in, the forcing instruments brought, upon which the sensible patient must submit to take whatever is administered. When the poor patient thus finds himself deprived of all communication with the world, and denied the use of pen and paper, all he can do is to compose himself under the unhappy situation in the hope of a more favourable report. But any composure under such affliction is immediately deemed a melancholy or sulky fit, by the waiter, who reports it as such to the doctor in the hearing of the despairing prisoner, whose misery is thus redoubled in finding that the doctor prescribes a repetition of the dose, and that from day to day, until the patient is so debilitated in body that in time it impairs his mind.

The Select Committee, whose members included the elder Pitt, Fox, Lord North, Grenville and Townshend, did not make a very thorough investigation. In fact, their inquiries concerned only two of the many madhouses, and even then they dealt only with one patient in each of these asylums. However, they reached the conclusion that "the present state of the private madhouses in this Kingdom requires the interposition of the legislature."

The legislature was very slow in making any "interposition." Eleven years elapsed before Parliament passed an Act for regulating private madhouses, and the scope of this was so limited that it had little effect.

CHAPTER X

THE SICK IN MIND
(continued)

As far as public asylums were concerned there were definite improvements during the second half of the eighteenth century. The Manchester Royal Lunatic Asylum was founded in 1766, the York Asylum in 1777, and the Liverpool Royal Lunatic Asylum in 1792. The Manchester Asylum was established by the Board of Trustees of the Public Infirmary, who had considered admitting lunatics when the infirmary was opened in 1752, but had then decided that this would lead to considerable difficulty. However, they had continued to discuss the matter frequently, as they were anxious to provide accommodation for "these unhappy wretches." The promise of generous contributions led them to resolve to add two wings to the infirmary, each containing twelve cells, with rooms for a governor and staff.

The asylum was opened in 1766 and during the first year thirty-two persons were admitted and thirteen of these were discharged cured. The following rule was made regarding admissions—

> No patient shall be taken into the Lunatick Hospital till an Order shall be made for his or her admittance in the Hospital Book, signed by the physician and four or more of the Trustees of the Infirmary at their Weekly Board, except in cases of emergency, when by an Order from one of the physicians, a patient may be admitted and retained till the Monday following only.

This regulation, together with the rule that a petition for the admission of a patient had to be signed by at least two of his friends or relations or by churchwardens or overseers of the poor, was designed to protect sane people from being sent to the asylum.

The treatment of the patients there was a little more humane than in most other mental hospitals of the time. Physical violence was forbidden, although chains were used. It was realised, however, that these might lead to ill effects by restricting the circulation and so the regulations provided that the feet of patients who were chained should be examined and gently rubbed every morning and evening, and covered with flannel during the winter. Sightseeing by curious people was not permitted. Those patients who behaved well were rewarded by being given small improvements in their amenities, and they were also allowed to walk in the large garden.

One of the physicians at the asylum wrote an account of the methods of treatment. From this we learn that blood-letting was used in young and plethoric maniacs whose eyes were inflamed, who passed the night without sleep, and whose pulse was rapid. However, too much blood-letting might reduce the patient to an irrevocable state. Vomiting was usually employed, since the stomach was often deranged in cases of mania, and for this purpose tartar emetic was administered. Purgatives were considered useful, and calomel was given until the patient's mouth was sore. Opium, bark and wine were also used liberally. Repeated bathing was considered very effective; cold water was used for melancholy patients and warm water for maniacs. It might require five or six men to put a maniac into the bath, but after being immersed for half an hour or so he would be so submissive that one attendant could return him to his bed. Running sores were supposed to let the "bad humours" out of a person and for this reason they were produced artificially and kept open.

The most important step forward during the eighteenth century was undoubtedly the opening of the Retreat, at York. In 1791 friends of a patient in the asylum in that city tried to visit her, but they were refused admission. This made them suspect that she was being ill-treated and soon afterwards she died in circumstances which confirmed their suspicions. This led to a proposal by William Tuke, an influential member of the Society of Friends, that an institution should be founded where there would be no concealment and where the patients should be treated as kindly as possible. Tuke laid his plan before his fellow

Quakers, who gave it their approval and subscribed sufficient
money to buy eleven acres of land and erect the Retreat, which
was opened in 1796. It was given this name "to convey the idea
of what such an institution should be, namely a place in which the
unhappy might obtain a refuge, a quiet haven in which the shat-
tered bark might find the means of reparation or of safety."

At first Tuke himself lived at the Retreat and supervised its
administration, but he was soon fortunate in engaging a man
named George Jepson as superintendent. Jepson's wife acted as
matron, and these two were employed at the Retreat until 1823.
The success of the venture owed much to them. In addition to the
Jepsons there were five other members of the staff to care for the
thirty patients. A charge was made for each patient, varying from
eight to fifteen shillings weekly, according to the type of accommodation which they occupied. Patients were allowed to
bring their servants into the Retreat for the payment of an additional six shillings a week.

The treatment was quite different from that at other mental
establishments. The patients were never punished; they were
trusted to a far greater extent than in other asylums; invited to tea
parties given by the matron; encouraged to engage in work, such
as gardening or sewing; provided with a library; allowed to
attend the religious meetings of the Society of Friends; and some
of them had their meals at the superintendent's table. A good idea
of conditions at the Retreat can be obtained from the following
account written by a visitor—

> At the Retreat they sometimes have patients brought to them
> frantic and in irons, whom they at once release, and by mild argu-
> ments and gentle arts reduce almost immediately to obedience and
> orderly behaviour. A great deal of delicacy appears in the attentions
> paid to the smaller feelings of the patients. The iron bars which
> guarded the windows have been avoided, and neat iron sashes,
> having all the appearance of wooden ones, have been substituted in
> their places; and when I visited them, the managers were occupied
> in contriving how to get rid of the bolts with which the patients are
> shut up at night on account of their harsh, ungrateful sound, and of
> their communicating to the asylum somewhat of the air and character

of a prison. The effects of such attentions, both on the happiness of the patients and the discipline of the institution, are more important than may at first view be imagined. Attachment to the place and to the managers, and an air of comfort and of contentment, rarely exhibited within the precincts of such establishments, are consequently easily discovered in the general demeanour of the patients.

Meanwhile there seems to have been some improvement in conditions at Bethlem, to judge by the favourable manner in which a Frenchman who visited the hospital in 1788 compared it with hospitals in his own country—

> I stayed for some time in Bedlam. The poor creatures there are not chained up in dark cellars, stretched on damp ground, nor reclining on cold paving stones, when a moment of reason succeeds to delirium. When they seem to be awakening from a long dream, there is nothing to recall their pitiable condition—no bolts, no bars. The doors are open, their rooms wainscoted, and long airy corridors give them a chance of exercise. A cleanliness hardly conceivable unless seen reigns in this hospital. Five or six men maintain this cleanliness, assisted by the patients themselves, who are rewarded by small presents.

It seems doubtful, however, whether this glowing account was a true picture of conditions in Bethlem, for in 1814 a very different state of affairs was revealed. A member of a group of philanthropists who made it a practice to visit asylums from time to time happened to go to Bethlem, where he saw a patient named Norris. Norris had tried to murder several people, including his keeper, and it was therefore deemed necessary to keep him under restraint. He could slip out of ordinary handcuffs, so the governors had a special apparatus made for him. An iron ring several inches wide was riveted round his neck and fastened by a chain to a ring which was allowed to slide upwards and downwards on an upright iron bar. Another iron bar was riveted round his body, with circular projections which enclosed his arms and pinioned them to his sides. This apparatus made it just possible for him to stand up or to lie on his back, but he could not move more than a step away from the wall. Norris was confined in this manner for nine years, although for much of this time he

was quite rational, as several Members of Parliament discovered
when they went to see him. Their indignation and that of many
other people led to his release, but he was in an advanced stage of
tuberculosis, and died within a few months.

The publicity which the Norris case attracted led the House of
Commons to set up another Select Committee. This committee
made thorough investigations into the conditions at a number of
asylums and also in private madhouses, besides dealing with the
treatment of pauper lunatics in workhouses. From their volumin-
ous reports it appeared that the conditions in which the insane
were forced to live did not vary greatly in different parts of the
country.

In their inquiry regarding Bethlem the committee were informed by the apothecary that the surgeon, who had just died,
had himself been "generally insane and mostly drunk" for ten
years, and had on a number of occasions been placed in a strait
jacket. There is reason to doubt whether all the evidence given
by the apothecary was true; his own behaviour had by no means
been above reproach, for he frequently absented himself from the
hospital for days on end, and his visits usually lasted no longer
than half an hour. The physician also admitted that he seldom
toured the hospital to see the patients. The steward was over
eighty years old and was "gradually declining."

One of the persons who gave evidence to the committee was
the man who had first drawn attention to the case of Norris. He
told them of other patients he had seen during the same visit—

> We first proceeded to visit the women's galleries: one of the
> side rooms contained about ten patients, each chained by one arm
> or leg to the wall; the chain allowing them merely to stand up by
> the bench or form fixed to the wall, or to sit down on it. The naked-
> ness of each patient was covered by a blanket-gown only; the blanket-
> gown is a blanket formed something like a dressing-gown, with
> nothing to fasten with in front; this constitutes the whole covering:
> the feet even were naked.
> In the men's wing in the side room, six patients were chained
> close to the wall, five handcuffed, and one locked to the wall by
> the right arm as well as the right leg; he was very noisy; all were

naked except as to the blanket-gown or a small rug on the shoulders, and without shoes: one complained much of the coldness of his feet; one of us felt them—they were very cold. The patients in this room, except the noisy one and the poor lad with cold feet, who was lucid when we saw him, were dreadful idiots; their nakedness and their mode of confinement gave this room the appearance of a dog-kennel.

Evidence regarding the York Asylum was given by a West Riding magistrate. He described the condition of four cells each about eight feet square—

The walls were daubed with excrement; the air-holes, of which there were one in each cell, were partly filled with it. In one cell there were two pewter chamber-pots, loose. I asked the keeper if these cells were inhabited by the patients, and was told they were at night. I then desired him to take me upstairs and show me the place of the women who came out of those cells that morning; I then went upstairs and he showed me into a room, which I caused him to measure, and the size of which, he told me, was twelve feet by seven feet ten inches; and in which there were thirteen women, who, he told me, had all come out of those cells that morning.

For information regarding pauper lunatics the committee interviewed a banker named Henry Alexander, who had visited nearly fifty workhouses. He described how, at Liskeard, he had seen two women chained to a damp stone floor; they were not allowed any water for washing. At Tavistock he had great difficulty in persuading the master to allow him to see the cells where three lunatics were kept. He was told that the cells were unfit for anybody to visit, although they had been cleaned that morning. He at last managed to make the master give way and let him enter one of the cells. He told the committee: "I never smelt such a stench in my life, and it was so bad that a friend who went with us said he could not enter the other. . . . The stench was so great I felt almost suffocated; and for hours after, if I ate anything, I still retained the same smell; I could not get rid of it; and it should be remembered that these cells had been washed out that morning, and the doors had been opened some hours previous."

The committee visited a number of private madhouses, in-

cluding an establishment at Hoxton which had nearly five
hundred patients. Some of them were sailors, for this madhouse
had been selected by the Navy as a place to which insane seamen
could be sent. The committee discovered a terrible state of affairs:
the patients slept two in a bed; only about thirty of them had any
medical treatment, and these were persons who were fortunate
enough to be visited by their own doctors; and their food consisted almost wholly of beef and beer. At another madhouse the
committee were told that a patient had been kept for several
months in a box whose base was about four feet square. During
the whole of this time he had been naked, and air could reach
him only through a few holes in the top of the box.

The Select Committee's report led to some improvements, but
no new legislation was passed except for an unimportant Act
empowering Justices of the Peace to send pauper lunatics to
county asylums or to private institutions.

In 1815 Bethlem had been moved to St. George's Fields, for
the magnificent structure of 1676 had become so insecure that
there was not a level floor or an upright wall in the whole place.
Yet less than seven years previously, when negotiations for a new
site were already under way, at the request of the Home
Secretary new blocks had been erected to accommodate criminal
lunatics of both sexes.

In 1816 one of the hospital's governors proposed that a chaplain should be appointed. For a period of nearly forty years commencing in 1675 the chaplains of Bridewell had visited Bethlem
five times weekly, but in 1713 the governors had decided that the
"visitation of Bethlem was quite unnecessary." The new proposal
was strongly opposed by the physicians, who said that some insane persons were adversely affected by hearing readings from the
Bible. However, a few services were held as an experiment, and
when this proved successful the chaplain of King Edward's School
was engaged to act as chaplain of Bethlem. It was not until 1856
that the hospital had its own chaplain.

Other improvements were gradually introduced during the
forty years following the inquiry of 1815. In the eighteen-

twenties the women sat in their garden during the summer or played battledore and shuttlecock; in the winter they read or listened to a barrel organ. The men played football or other games. By 1840 the pastimes included dominoes, cards, knitting, tailoring, and even little dances. Within a few more years there were a billiard table and a piano, and in the eighteen-fifties regular social evenings were organised, although the sexes were not allowed to mix at these.

In 1823 somebody writing under the guise of "A Constant Observer" published *Sketches in Bedlam*. He said that the patients had to rise at six o'clock in the summer and an hour later in the winter. Breakfast was at 8 a.m., dinner at 1 p.m., and supper at 6 p.m. Two hours later the patients were locked up for the night. Every patient had a separate room, with a bed and sheets, except those in the basement, who still had to sleep on straw. The patients could be visited by their relatives once a week.

The dietary still left much to be desired. Breakfast consisted of gruel and bread, and supper of bread and butter. The dinner was of meat and bread; sometimes soup or broth was substituted for meat. The only thing which was supplied to the patients unsparingly was beer.

The patients were not allowed to cut up their own food, for until 1848 it was thought that they could not be trusted with steel knives and forks. Their meat was cut into strips by the keepers, and then they were allowed to break it into pieces of suitable size with bone knives and forks. Crockery was not introduced until 1844; prior to that date the patients had to use wooden bowls and spoons.

Mechanical restraint was still used, but every instance had to be recorded, and the records were read weekly to a sub-committee of the Board of Governors. Padded cells were installed in 1844, after they had been in use in Germany for more than thirty years.

The first resident physician was not appointed until 1853. Prior to that date the medical staff had consisted of two non-resident physicians, a surgeon and an apothecary. Both the physicians had large general practices and devoted only a few hours weekly to work at the hospital.

There had been similar improvements at St. Luke's. Mechanical restraint was gradually reduced, but even in 1840 the physicians said it could not be abandoned altogether; to do so would be "fallacious, experimental and hazardous." But these same physicians urged the committee to provide the patients with such amenities as reading rooms, a piano, bagatelle and playing cards. After Waterloo increasing costs had caused the admission charges to be raised to £3 for middle-class patients, £6 for parish patients, and seven shillings a week for incurables, but in 1831 these were reduced to £1, £4 and six shillings respectively.

By 1823 nine counties had asylums; they were at Nottingham, Bedford, Norwich, Lancaster, Stafford, Wakefield, Bodmin, Lincoln and Gloucester. The largest, that at Wakefield, had accommodation for 250 patients; the smallest, at Lincoln, could take only fifty. The superintendents of several of these establishments were paid a certain sum in respect of each patient, and from the total amount thus received they had to meet all the costs. At Bodmin the payment was fourteen shillings per patient per week. The superintendents were allowed to take private patients. Sometimes they were medical men, but at Stafford, where there were 120 patients, there was a lay superintendent who was paid £200 a year and a part-time physician who received the same salary. The other staff consisted of a matron, whose salary was £40 a year, two keepers (one male, one female), who each received £25, and a porter, who was paid £15 and provided with a suit of clothes and a hat. The food at most of the asylums, although plain, appears to have been plentiful. Most of the patients had beds, although in one or two of the asylums they had to sleep on straw. They were encouraged to work in the kitchens and gardens.

In 1827 yet another Select Committee was set up; this time it was to consider the state of pauper lunatics in the Metropolis. The members seem to have regarded their task as an urgent one, for they issued their report only sixteen days after they were appointed. It showed that conditions in the private houses were quite as bad as, or even worse than, those revealed in the public asylums by the earlier report. An ex-patient said that in one madhouse the patients were locked in their cribs or bedsteads from three o'clock in the afternoon until nine o'clock the following morning. At weekends they were chained in these cribs from Saturday afternoon until Monday morning, when they were taken into the yard and the excrement which had accumulated on their bodies was washed off with a mop dipped in cold water. A surgeon whose duty it was to visit the pauper lunatics from his parish said of another madhouse, where nine shillings a week was charged for the maintenance of each patient: "I scarcely ever go there but I do not find someone that is lingering about the yard in a half-dying state that ought to be in bed. They are entirely at the mercy of the keepers."

The report led to the passing of two Acts of Parliament in 1828. One of these dealt with improvements to the county asylums and the other set up a new body, the Metropolitan Commissioners in Lunacy, to be responsible for the control of madhouses in the Metropolis. It also provided that every madhouse with more than one hundred patients was to have a resident medical officer, and those with less than a hundred patients had to be visited by a doctor at least twice a week. It is strange to find that there were no similar provisions for county asylums. Most of them did, in fact, have a resident medical officer, but at Norwich one was not appointed until fifteen years after the 1828 Act.

The Metropolitan Commissioners—one of whom was Lord Ashley, later to become the famous philanthropist Earl of Shaftesbury—did their work well. Their visits to the madhouses brought about many improvements, including such things as additional baths and new kitchens. Yet conditions in many of them were still very bad. In 1846, according to a report issued by the Commissioners, there were some madhouses where breakfast and supper consisted only of bread and skimmed milk. In many of the asylums in the provinces there was no improvement at all; this was largely due to the fact that the Justices of the Peace, who

were legally responsible for visiting the madhouses, sadly
neglected their duty. Even in the eighteen-forties there were some
madhouses without baths. In one large asylum several of the
women patients were chained to their beds, naked or with only
a rug to cover them, even in December. At the same place only
one towel was provided each week to be used by 107 patients.

During the fifteen years which followed the legislation of 1828
a number of new county asylums were built. One of these, the
Middlesex Asylum at Hanwell, could accommodate one thousand
patients and was the largest in the country. With the much smaller
asylum at Lincoln it led the way in the practice of non-restraint.
This was a revolutionary idea, for it meant that no mechanical
restraint whatever was used. The change was brought about
gradually; it began at Lincoln in 1829, but it was not until 1838
that all restraint there was abolished. The two men responsible
for this great innovation were the visiting physician, Dr. Charlesworth, and the house surgeon, Mr. Gardiner Hill. Of course,
there still had to be some means of controlling violent patients,
and they could still be placed in solitary confinement or, if
necessary, held down by the attendants. To make violence less
likely, a new type of attendant was engaged—strong men and
trained nurses. To attract such people to Lincoln, the wages were
increased. Other measures were also taken to reduce the possibility of violence—liquor was banned, and the patients were
made to take plenty of exercise, so that they would have little
energy left for the use of force against the attendants. This
system, accompanied by other improvements, was a great success.
One woman patient wrote the following description of conditions
at Lincoln in a letter to a friend—

The nurses all seem very loving and dutiful to the patients. If your
finger only aches, the House Surgeon attends several times a day;
and at night if he sees any of them unruly, he orders a nurse to sit up
with them. The bedrooms are carpeted (feather beds, most of them
with hangings), wash-stands, basins, towels, looking-glass, comb and
brush, and a nurse to attend us. We have tea twice a day, and as much
toast as we can eat—milk and bread for our supper, meat dinners

every day, and different sorts of puddings. The Matron of the Asylum stands at the table, and asks whether we are all satisfied; and if anyone wants more, she orders a nurse to bring it.

The system of non-restraint was copied at Hanwell, where a further important step in the treatment of the insane was taken. The medical superintendent, Dr. Conolly, and the chaplain introduced the first educational classes for patients. The illiterate were taught to read and write, and those who could already read and write were instructed in singing, geography and drawing. Unfortunately these classes did not continue for long, because the Visiting Committee considered that their cost was an unnecessary expense.

In 1842 Parliament extended the duties of the Metropolitan Commissioners by directing that two Commissioners, one legal and one medical, were to visit all county asylums once a year and all provincial madhouses—or licensed houses, as they had been called for some time—twice a year. They were to make a report on their visits.

Only eighteen counties had asylums. These, with twelve voluntary hospitals and 136 licensed houses, provided accommodation for little more than half of the 21,000 people recorded as being insane. This lack of accommodation was chiefly due to the desire by public authorities to economise. The cost of building an asylum was more than £200 a bed, whereas to build a workhouse cost only £40 a bed, or less. Many of the asylums had become almost filled with incurable cases. At Hanwell, out of one thousand patients, only thirty were curable. The commissioners thought Hanwell was far too large: "No asylum for curable lunatics should contain more than 250 patients." They wanted the problem of accommodation to be tackled on a national basis: "Pauper lunatics have unfortunately become so numerous throughout the whole kingdom, that the proper construction and cost of asylums for their use has ceased to be a subject which affects a few counties only, and has become a matter of national interest and importance."

Nearly a hundred licensed madhouses outside the metropolitan area were inspected by the commissioners. An example of the way in which the Justices neglected their duties was shown by what occurred at West Auckland. The commissioners decided that the madhouse there was "entirely unfit for the reception of insane persons," yet on the same day as they made their inspection two Justices also visited it and made the following report: "We have this day visited the Asylum, and found the commissioners had just left it. We found everything in good order." At another licensed house, when they inquired why patients were chained by the leg to the floor, the commissioners were told that the purpose of this was "to see what they would do!"

The commissioners were able to report some great improvements in the licensed houses in London since they first started inspecting these. The houses which had been among the worst when they were examined by the Select Committee of 1827 were now commended: "We have visited few, if any, receptacles for the insane in which the patients are more kindly or more judiciously treated."

The report led to the passing in 1845 of two Acts of Parliament. One of these dealt with the management of county asylums and the other—the Lunatics Act—with the control of institutions. The Commissioners in Lunacy became a permanent body; six of them were to work full-time and be paid salaries of £1,500 a year; the other five were to be part-time and unpaid. They were to have a staff consisting of a secretary and two clerks. The commissioners had to visit all public hospitals except Bethlem at least once a year. (Bethlem was made subject to these inspections in 1853.) Three reports on their work had to be submitted during each year to the Lord Chancellor. The procedure for the certification of patients was tightened up and the safeguards against wrongful detention were increased. All institutions were required to keep records of admissions and discharges and of the use of restraint.

The next fifty years saw further improvements in both legislation and accommodation. The legislation consisted of various minor amending Acts and also the Lunacy Act of 1890, which consolidated all the previous laws relating to the care of the insane. One of its most important provisions provided that non-pauper patients could be admitted to a mental institution only on the order of a Justice of the Peace, a county court judge or a stipendiary magistrate. Previously there had been no judicial inquiry, and several cases of improper detention had caused great public concern.

The amount of accommodation was greatly increased, largely as a result of the Act of 1845 which required county and borough justices to provide asylums. By 1890 there was accommodation in asylums and elsewhere for over eighty thousand patients. The government had erected a State institution for criminal lunatics at Broadmoor; this was opened in 1863. Previously there had been no separate institutions for criminal lunatics, and they had been detained in the ordinary asylums. Special provision for the insane poor in London was made as a result of an Act of 1867 which established the Metropolitan Asylums Board. In addition to building asylums, the Board erected two institutions for mental defectives. There were already several other establishments for defectives, the first having been opened at Bath in 1846. An asylum for idiots had been opened at Highgate in 1848, and it was followed by the founding of several similar institutions in various parts of the country.

Since the beginnings of St. Luke's Hospital were described in the previous chapter, it may be of interest to look at the conditions there during the second half of the nineteenth century. In 1855 the commissioners commented on "the cheerless and dreary aspect presented both within the building and in the airing courts," and urged the need for a new hospital, but their recommendation could not be put into effect because there was insufficient money. In 1856 the Resident Medical Superintendent was made responsible for the general condition of the hospital and was, in effect, designated as the senior resident officer. Previously the steward had been regarded as the chief officer. In 1861 the commissioners found another cause for complaint—two patients were allowed to have a hot bath simultaneously. Seven years later the records show that there were seven male and twelve female attendants, with one night attendant for each sex. Their rates of pay varied according to their length of service; the highest wages paid to a male attendant were £32 10s. od. a year, while the best-paid female attendant received £24. The working hours were very unsatisfactory, for a system of doubling day and night duty was in operation whereby an attendant might work from 6 a.m. on one day until 8 p.m. on the next, with only four hours' rest during the whole of this time. In 1871 the commissioners expressed their pleasure at finding that the patients were given mustard and vinegar for the first time; they also noticed that green vegetables were provided three times a week. During the last decade of the century some attention was paid to improving the lot of the hard-worked staff. A billiard room was provided for the male attendants and a large sitting-room for the nurses.

Between the end of the nineteenth century and the passing of the National Health Service Act of 1946, the most important date in the history of the care of the insane was 1930, when the Mental Treatment Act was passed. This recognised the new outlook towards insanity by doing away with the terms "asylum," "pauper" and "lunatic"—and also with the stigma which had for long been associated with them—and replacing them by "mental hospital," "rate-aided person" and "person of unsound mind" respectively. It also introduced two new classes of patients who could be admitted to the hospitals without first being certified. These were temporary patients—those who were expected to regain their power of volition within six months—and voluntary patients, who entered the hospital of their own free will and could leave it again after giving three days' notice.

When the National Health Service Act of 1946 came into operation, it brought the mental hospitals under the same administrative control as the hospitals for physical illness. Both are now administered by the Regional Hospital Boards. Not all mental hospitals were brought into the National Health Service; for example, the Retreat, now classified as a registered hospital, remains outside. So, too, do the licensed houses, but the number of these has greatly decreased.

This chapter on the story of the mental hospitals cannot properly be closed without mentioning once again the two establishments to whose history a number of its pages were devoted. Bethlem Hospital is no longer in London, but has been moved to Beckenham in Kent and is classified as a teaching hospital. St. Luke's was also moved to a new site near Muswell Hill, and it lost its separate identity in 1948, when it was merged with the Middlesex Hospital.

CHAPTER XI

A NATIONAL HOSPITAL SERVICE

W HEN the National Health Service Act, 1946, came into force on 5th July, 1948, about 2,800 hospitals with some 450,000 beds were transferred to the control of the Minister of Health. For purposes of administration England and Wales were divided into fourteen regions, each with a Regional Hospital Board.

The value of hospital planning on a regional basis had been recognised long before the Act was passed. It had been impossible for the heterogeneous authorities who had previously administered the hospitals to give an adequate service throughout the country, and in 1937 the Sankey Commission had advocated that the voluntary hospitals should be grouped into regions. In 1946 the British Medical Association had issued a statement in which they said: "The Association joins with the Government in desiring a co-ordinated hospital service regionally administered over natural hospital areas."

It was believed that administration on a regional basis would enable the hospital service to be planned in such a way as to ensure that every area had adequate facilities. At the same time duplication, which was both wasteful and costly, would be avoided. A more equal distribution of consultants could also be achieved. In 1941 the Nuffield Provincial Hospital Trust had drawn attention to the fact that "the distribution of consultants and specialists has been extremely unequal; in some regions there are many, even if not enough; in others very few or none."

Under the scheme set up by the Act each Region was to be associated with at least one medical school and teaching hospital. This would enable the influence of the teaching hospital, as a centre of research, to be felt throughout the Region. It was hoped, too, that the standard of treatment in the teaching hospitals would be copied by all the other hospitals.

However, the teaching hospitals themselves were not to be administered by the Regional Hospital Boards. They were to have their own authorities, known as Boards of Governors. The Governors, who have under their control about 140 hospitals, are directly responsible to the Minister, and are appointed by him.

He also appoints the members of the Regional Hospital Boards, who have to collaborate with the Boards of Governors in their area in planning, providing and supervising a co-ordinated hospital and specialist service. The Regional Hospital Board decides the manner in which the hospitals shall be used, plans and carries out capital works, appoints senior medical staff, and provides such services as blood transfusion for the Region as a whole.

The day-to-day administration of the hospitals is in the hands of Hospital Management Committees, who are appointed by the Regional Hospital Boards. Each Board has divided the hospitals in its area into groups and each group has a Hospital Management Committee. Some of these Committees administer only one hospital—usually a large mental hospital. Most of the groups consist of between six and twenty hospitals, and there are a few— less than half a dozen—with more than twenty. The responsibilities of the Hospital Management Committees include the maintenance of the hospital premises, the purchase of equipment and supplies, and the appointment and dismissal of staff, except senior medical and dental staff. Hospital Management Committees may, if they wish, set up House Committees for individual hospitals, but these bodies are supposed to be mainly advisory.

This system of Boards and Committees has now been in operation long enough to enable its benefits and disadvantages to become apparent. It has enabled the hospital services of a region to be planned in the manner which best serves the needs of the population of the region as a whole. The Boards can arrange the purchase of very expensive equipment which would be beyond the financial resources of individual hospitals and groups, and ensure that this equipment is available for all patients in the region. The services of consultants can be distributed so that the best medical knowledge and advice is obtainable by everybody.

The new system has worked reasonably well. It has its faults, of course, and these have been realised, but no sweeping changes have been made. A number of committees have been set up by the governments who have been in power since 1948 to enquire into various aspects of the new hospital service, but, for the most part, they have not advocated any major changes in the pattern of administration. The general view was summarised in the Report of the Committee of Enquiry into the Cost of the National Health Service: "Some of the strains and stresses of the National Health Service are attributed to the difficulty experienced by many, who had grown up under the old system, when called upon to operate a service administered on different lines. Longer experience of the working of the Service and the grateful emergence of a new generation may make comparatively simple many things which now appear difficult or impracticable."

From its commencement the new service has been handicapped by financial limitations. At first there was an enthusiastic burst of planning and spending. It seemed that the lack of money which had hampered most of the hospitals under the old system was over. But the "honeymoon period," as the chairman of one of the new hospital authorities called it, was soon over. The government clamped down on spending. It had little alternative, for the contribution which the Exchequer had to make towards expenditure on the Health Service in 1949 amounted to more than £387,000,000. Since then the cost, like that of most things, has increased tremendously. In the first ten years it went up by 69 per cent. That was for the Health Service as a whole. In the case of the hospital service alone it was considerably greater: 92 per cent. Yet not one complete new hospital was built. In the first five years there was only about £50,000,000 for capital development. According to the Ministry of Health "the main story of hospital capital development in the first five years of the National Health Service is of scarce resources carefully husbanded so as to bring maximum results at the minimum cost, to make good as much damage and obsolescence as possible and to provide modest extensions here and there where the need was greatest."

How did the great change of 5th July, 1948, affect the hospitals themselves and the people who worked in them? The effects on three hospitals—local authority, voluntary and mental—have been recounted in the Acton Society Trust's booklet *The Impact of the Change*. The impact was greatest on the voluntary hospital, which lost its independence and became one of a number of units in a group. The other two types of hospitals had both been administered by local authorities, so that under the new system their control passed from one public body to another. Administration by a Hospital Management Committee is more decentralised than that of a local authority. Within the hospitals themselves it was the senior officers who felt the impact of the change most keenly. Particularly was this the case with the Medical Superintendent of the former local authority hospital: he lost much of his administrative power, which he now had to share with the Matron and the Secretary. Similarly, in the former voluntary hospital the Secretary gained in management power at the expense of the Matron. In most hospitals there were now more specialist officers, such as domestic supervisors and catering officers, and some of the Matrons' functions were transferred to them. This left the Matrons with more time for the supervision of the nursing staff, which should be their prime duty, yet many of them did not welcome the loss of power and responsibility.

Among the general public there were many critics of the National Health Service Act who felt that its passing would mean the end of the voluntary spirit which had done so much for the hospitals through so many centuries. These critics were soon shown to be wrong. For example, the ten thousand members of the Boards and Committees who administer the hospitals are all unpaid volunteers. Then today many hospitals have attached to them bodies known as Leagues of Friends. There is a National League of Hospital Friends with more than five hundred local leagues affiliated to it. The members of these leagues carry out various kinds of personal services for the patients, such as shopping for them and visiting those who have no friends or relatives. By organising fêtes, whist drives, etc., they raise money for items which the Hospital Management Committees may not be able to afford from their limited budgets. These include such things as television sets, telephone trolleys, and bed curtains. Some leagues have also embarked upon quite large schemes, such as the erection of recreation halls and chapels.

In the first three years of the National Health Service the number of staffed beds in hospitals increased by about 23,000. Between 1948 and 1950 the average daily bed occupation rose from 382,600 to 402,600. This increase in the numbers able to receive hospital treatment was accompanied by various improvements, such as better catering and a higher standard of comfort in the wards of many hospitals. People have been able to receive specialist treatment in hospitals and in their homes without having to meet the heavy expenditure of specialists' fees. Many of those who have received care would probably have had no treatment at all if there had been no National Health Service. There continues to be plenty of room for improvement, of course, and there is no doubt that progress would have been far greater if more money had been available.

The past twenty years or so have seen great improvements in methods of treatment and changes in the incidence of disease. These have brought changes in the way in which some hospitals are used. Tuberculosis, which at one time filled the sanatoria, is now attacked by new drugs, so that the length of time that tuberculous patients have to receive hospital treatment has greatly decreased. Consequently sanatoria are now used for surgical cases of various kinds. There has been a marked decline in fevers, so fever hospitals are used for other purposes, too. Smallpox has almost disappeared, and many of the tiny hospitals which used to be kept in isolated spots ready for sudden outbreaks of the dread disease have been closed. The lock hospitals have closed, too, because specific cures have been found for venereal diseases.

The National Health Service has helped to bring about a great decrease in the number of private hospitals and nursing homes. Most of these were established from 1880 onwards to meet a demand for hospital accommodation for those who could afford to pay for it or did not wish to receive treatment in the public hospitals. The National Health Service has improved the standard of the latter, and people are not so reluctant to enter them. For those who want more privacy than they would normally get in a hospital ward, the National Health Service Act has provided private and amenity beds, for which the patient pays the full cost or part of the cost respectively.

Lack of funds has meant a severe limitation on new hospital construction. The rebuilding of bomb-damaged St. Thomas's Hospital did not commence until fifteen years after the end of the Second World War. The construction of a new Guy's Hospital costing well over £2,000,000 began in 1957. At Swindon the first stage of a completely new hospital, the Princess Margaret Hospital, was opened in 1959. These are three of the major developments in hospital construction and reconstruction under the new era. They incorporate new ideas which should avoid the institutional character typical of so many of the older hospitals. Yet some of these ideas are quite simple. For example, in the new St. Thomas's Hospital the beds are to be placed parallel to the windows to allow the patients to see as much as possible of the fine view over the River Thames. The beds will be arranged in bays of four, so that every patient will have a corner position and thus enjoy a little more privacy than in most hospitals, and yet not be isolated. Instead of a large waiting-hall for all the out-patients, there will be small comfortable waiting-rooms near the various clinics. In the Princess Margaret Hospital, too, a large central waiting-hall has been avoided by providing as waiting areas alcoves off the main corridors, and each alcove has a pleasant view over the countryside or looks out on to a small garden courtyard. To reduce the work of the nursing staff there is a wash-basin between each pair of beds.

Other ideas incorporated in the new hospitals are the result of modern scientific ingenuity. At Guy's there are pneumatic tubes for conveying prescriptions, etc., from one department to another, and in the wards there are telephone points so that a telephone can be wheeled on a trolley to every patient. There are ten operating theatres, which are provided with twenty-four changes of completely fresh, filtered, washed and warmed air every hour.

The creation of a National Health Service has not meant the end of the independent hospitals. About two hundred voluntary hospitals, with ten thousand beds, were not brought into the new scheme. They were mostly rather small institutions belonging to religious bodies or serving certain small sections of the population. Included among them were the Retreat at York, the Royal Masonic Hospital, the Manor House Hospital, which belongs to the Trade Unions, and King Edward VII Sanatorium at Midhurst. Private nursing homes were also left outside the National Health Service. Patients who receive treatment under the Service are, however, sometimes admitted to these private hospitals and homes, for the Regional Hospital Boards have entered into contractual arrangements with a large number of them.

Since 1948 one independent hospital has been founded outside the National Health Service. According to its founders it was established "to meet a local need and to right a local wrong." The story really commences in 1899, when the Victoria Hospital at Kingston-on-Thames was opened. Nearly fifty years later, like hundreds of other cottage hospitals, it was transferred to the National Health Service, and in 1949 the South-West Metropolitan Regional Hospital Board decided that it should cease to be a general hospital and be converted into a gynaecological annexe of Kingston Hospital. This brought forth strong protests from the local inhabitants, particularly the general practitioners, and the Kingston and Malden Victoria Medical Foundation was established to raise funds for a new voluntary hospital. In seven years about £35,000 was collected. A country house at New Malden was purchased and £10,000 was spent in converting it into a hospital with twenty-one beds. In 1958 it was opened as the New Victoria Hospital. The local general practitioners, who were largely responsible for its establishment, give their services free.

How do the patients fare in the new hospital service compared with their counterparts of previous ages, or even with those of the first half of the present century? Generally speaking, there is a real attempt on the part of all concerned with their welfare to do everything possible for their comfort, both of body and of mind. There are fewer restrictions than there used to be. No longer are the patients awakened at 5 a.m.; 6 a.m. or 6.30 a.m. is more usual, and at one London teaching hospital the patients are not roused until 7 a.m. The matron of that hospital summed up a trend that is slowly becoming more widespread when she said: "I feel that patients should be allowed to follow as closely as possible the routine to which they are accustomed in their lives at home."

For those capable of enjoying them there are film shows, television and radio to relieve the monotony of illness. There are hospital libraries to provide books for entertainment and education, and hospital shops to cater for the patients' needs. Since bedridden people cannot go to the shop, the shop has to be taken to them. A selection of goods is displayed on a trolley, which is pushed from ward to ward and from bed to bed. This is a service which is often performed by one of the voluntary bodies, such as the Red Cross, the Women's Voluntary Service, or the League of Friends. In many hospitals the library is provided by the Order of St. John and the British Red Cross Society, who have combined to set up a Joint Committee for this purpose. The hospital authorities are called upon to make a contribution towards the costs, based on the number of occupied beds, and to reimburse the librarians' salaries.

The British Red Cross Society also organise a picture library service for long-term patients, mainly those in chest, mental and orthopaedic hospitals. About twelve thousand reproductions of paintings by well-known artists are circulated among more than five hundred hospitals. The Society's representatives make frequent visits to the hospitals to change the pictures, taking the opportunity to discuss them with the patients, who are able to choose the pictures.

Another service often provided by voluntary bodies enables patients to speak to their loved ones far away. A telephone is taken around the ward on a trolley; the ward has to be specially wired for this purpose, so that the telephone can be plugged in at various points.

How do the hospitals stand at the beginning of 1961, twelve years after they became the property—and the responsibility—of the nation? No new hospital has been built for more than twenty years, although construction work costing £100,000,000 is in progress. Nearly half the existing hospitals are over fifty years old, and six hundred were built more than a century ago. A very large number were originally workhouses.

There is continual concern over the increasing cost of the hospital service, yet there are many people who believe that even more should be spent. In 1959–60 the total cost was £394,913,000 —over £33,000,000 more than in the previous twelve months. All those who work in hospitals know that there is so much more that could be done. Fortunately the prospect now looks a little brighter, for in January, 1961, the Minister of Health announced that he had approved the construction of a number of new hospitals. He also put forward a ten-year plan for modernising the hospital service at a cost of about £500,000,000.

BIBLIOGRAPHY

ABEL-SMITH, BRIAN. *A History of the Nursing Profession.* Heinemann, 1960.

ABRAHAM, J. J. *Lettsom.* Heinemann, 1933.

ACTON SOCIETY TRUST. *Hospitals and the State: Background and Blueprint.* 1955. *Hospitals and the State: The Impact of the Change.* 1956.

ADAMS, H. P. *Cottage Hospitals.*

BALL, J. M. *The Sack-'em-Up Men.* Oliver and Boyd, 1928.

BARNES, STANLEY. *The Birmingham Hospitals Centre.* Stanford and Mann, Birmingham, 1953.

BISHOP, W. J. *The Early History of Surgery.* Robert Hale, 1960.

BLOMFIELD, J. *St. George's 1733–1933.* Medici Society, 1933.

BRIDE, J. W. *A Short History of the St. Mary's Hospitals, Manchester.* Sherratt and Hughes, Manchester, 1922.

BRITISH MEDICAL ASSOCIATION. *A General Medical Service for the Nation.* 1938. *Statement on Hospital Policy.* 1938.

BROCKBANK, E. M. *A Short History of Cheadle Royal from its Foundation in 1766.* Sherratt and Hughes, Manchester, 1934.

BROCKBANK, WILLIAM. *Portrait of a Hospital, 1752–1948.* Heinemann, 1952.

BURDETT, SIR HENRY. *Hospitals and Asylums of the World.* Churchill, 1891–93. *Cottage Hospitals: General, Fever and Convalescent with 50 beds and under.* Scientific Press. *Pay Hospitals of the World. Hospitals and Charities.*

CALDER, J. M. *The Story of Nursing.* Methuen, 1954.

CAMERON, H. C. *Joseph Lister, the Friend of Man.* Heinemann, 1948. *Mr. Guy's Hospital, 1726–1948.* Longmans, Green, 1954.

CANNINGS, RALPH B. *The City of London Maternity Hospital: A Short History.* 1922.

CHALMERS, R. W. *Hospitals and the State.* Bale, Sons and Danielson.

CLAY, ANDREW M. *A Short History of the Hospital for Women at Leeds, 1853–1953.* United Leeds Hospitals, 1953.

CLAY, ROTHA M. *The Mediaeval Hospitals of England.* Methuen, 1909.

COLLINS, E. TREACHER. *The History and Traditions of Moorfields Eye Hospital.* Lewis, 1929.

CONSTANT OBSERVER, A. *Sketches in Bedlam.* 1823.

COOK, E. T. *The Life of Florence Nightingale.* Macmillan, 1913.

COPE, SIR ZACHARY. *Florence Nightingale and the Doctors.* Museum Press, 1958.

CORRY, J. *History of Macclesfield*. 1817.

CREIGHTON, CHARLES. *A History of Epidemics in Britain*. C.U.P., 1891.

DAVIDSON, M. and ROUVRAY, F. G. *The Brompton Hospital, the Story of a Great Adventure*. Lloyd-Luke, 1955.

DUNN, C. L. (editor). *The Emergency Medical Services*. Vol. I. *England and Wales*. H.M.S.O., 1952.

EVANS, A. D. and HOWARD, L. G. R. *The Romance of the British Voluntary Hospital Movement*. Hutchinson, 1930.

FRAZER, W. M. *A History of English Public Health, 1834–1939*. Baillière, Tindall and Cox, 1950.

FRENCH, C. H. *The Story of St. Luke's Hospital, 1750–1948*. Heinemann, 1951.

GIBSON, ALEXANDER G. *The Radcliffe Infirmary*. O.U.P., 1926.

GODFREY, W. H. *The English Almshouse*. Faber and Faber, 1955.

GOULDING, B. *An Historical Account of St. Thomas's Hospital*. 1819.

GUTHRIE, DOUGLAS. *A History of Medicine*. Nelson, 1945.

HALLIDAY, SIR ANDREW. *A General View of the Present State of Lunatics and Lunatic Asylums in Great Britain and Ireland, and in Some Other Kingdoms*. 1828.

HEARNSHAW, F. J. C. *The Centenary History of King's College, London*. Harrap, 1929.

HIGGINS, T. T. *Great Ormond Street 1852–1952*. Odhams, 1952.

HOLE, CHRISTINA. *English Home Life 1500–1800*. Batsford, 1947. *The English Housewife in the Seventeenth Century*. Chatto and Windus, 1953.

HOWARD, JOHN. *Lazarettos and Hospitals*. 1789.

HUNT, H. C. *A Retired Habitation. A History of the Retreat, York*. Lewis, 1932.

IVES, A. G. L. *British Hospitals*. Collins, 1948.

JACOBS, F. H. *A History of the General Hospital, Nottingham*. Wright, Bristol, 1951.

JEWESBURY, ERIC C. O. *The Royal Northern Hospital 1856–1956*. Lewis, 1956.

JONES, KATHLEEN. *Lunacy, Law and Conscience*. Routledge and Kegan Paul, 1955.

JONES, E. WHEATLEY. *The History of the Manchester Northern Hospital for Women and Children*. 1933.

KERSHAW, RICHARD. *Story of Specialist Hospitals*.

LAMMOND, D. *Florence Nightingale*. 1935.

LANGDON-DAVIES, J. *Westminster Hospital 1719–1948*. Murray, 1952.

LONDON COUNTY COUNCIL. *The L.C.C. Hospitals—a Retrospect*. Staples Press, 1949.

LONG, FRANK D. *History of the King's Fund, 1897–1942.* King Edward's Hospital Fund for London, 1942.

LYLE, H. WILLOUGHBY. *King's and Some King's Men.* 1935.

MACALISTER, CHARLES J. *The Origin and History of the Liverpool Royal Southern Hospital.* Jones, 1936.

MCMENEMEY, W. H. *A History of the Worcester Royal Infirmary.* Press Alliances, 1947.

MACPHERSON, SIR W. G. *History of the Great War: Medical Services General History,* Vol. I. H.M.S.O., 1921.

MOORE, SIR NORMAN. *The History of St. Bartholomew's Hospital.* Pearson, 1918.

MORRIS, SIR ERNEST. *A History of the London Hospital.* Arnold, 1926.

MORRAH, DERMOT. *The British Red Cross.* Collins, 1944.

MUNRO, JOHN. *Low Life—or One Half of the World Does Not Know How the Other Half Lives.* 1752.

NIGHTINGALE, FLORENCE. *Notes on Hospitals.* 1859. *Notes on Lying-in Institutions.* 1871.

NUFFIELD PROVINCIAL HOSPITALS TRUST. *The Hospital Surveys—The Domesday Book of the Hospital Service.* 1946.

NUTTING, M. A. and DOCK, L. L. *A History of Nursing.* Putnam, 1907–12.

O'DONOGHUE, E. G. *The Story of Bethlehem Hospital.* Unwin, 1914.

O'MALLEY, T. B. *Florence Nightingale, 1820–1856.* Thornton Butterworth, 1931.

OPPERT, F. *Hospitals and Dispensaries.* 1887.

PARSONS, F. G. *The History of St. Thomas's Hospital.* Methuen, 1932–36.

PAVEY, AGNES E. *The Story of the Growth of Nursing.* Faber, 1938.

PEACHEY, G. C. *A History of St. George's Hospital.* 1910–14.

POLITICAL AND ECONOMIC PLANNING. *The British Health Services.* 1937.

POWELL, SIR ALLAN. *The Metropolitan Asylums Board and Its Work, 1867–1930.*

POWER and WARING. *A Short History of St. Bartholomew's Hospital 1123–1923.* St. Bartholomew's Hospital, 1923.

RAWES, WILLIAM. *History of St. Luke's.* 1904.

RENAUD, F. *A Short History of the House of Recovery.* Garnett and Evans, Manchester, 1885. *A Short History of the Rise and Progress of the Manchester Royal Infirmary.* Cornish, Manchester, 1898.

RIESMAN, D. *The Story of Medicine in the Middle Ages.* 1935.

RIPMAN, H. A. (editor). *Guy's Hospital 1725–1948.* Guy's Hospital Gazette Committee, 1951.

RODGERS, JOHN. *York.* Batsford, 1951.

ROSS, JAMES STIRLING. *The National Health Service in Great Britain—an*

Historical and Descriptive Study. Geoffrey Cumberlege, O.U.P., 1952.

RYAN, THOMAS. *History of Queen Charlotte's Lying-In Hospital.* Queen Charlotte's Hospital, 1885.

SAUNDERS, H. ST. G. *The Middlesex Hospital 1745–1948.* Parrish, 1949.

SEYMER, LUCY R. *A General History of Nursing.* 1949.

SKINNER, E. F. *A Short History of the Sheffield Royal Hospital, 1832–1932.* 1932.

SMITH, G. MUNRO. *A History of the Bristol Royal Infirmary.* Arrowsmith, Bristol, 1917.

SOUTH, J. F. *Memorials of the Craft of Surgery in England.* Cassell, 1886.

TAYLOR, F. SHERWOOD. *The Century of Science.* Heinemann, 1940.

TITMUSS, R. M. *Problems of Social Policy.* H.M.S.O., 1950.

TOOLEY, S. *The History of Nursing in the British Empire.* Bonsfield, 1906. *Life of Florence Nightingale.* 1905.

TUKE, D. H. *Chapters in the History of the Insane in the British Isles.* Kegan Paul, 1882.

TUKE, S. *Description of the Retreat at York.* York, 1813. *Review of the Early History of the Retreat.* 1846.

TURNER, E. S. *Call the Doctor.* Michael Joseph, 1959.

WALSH, J. J. *Mediaeval Medicine.* 1920.

WATKIN, P. J. *Lambeth Hospital. Fifty Years Retrospect.* Lambeth Group Hospital Management Committee, 1954.

WHITCOMBE, GEORGE. *The General Infirmary at Gloucester—Its Past and Present.* 1903.

WHITNEY, JANET. *Elizabeth Fry.* Harrap, 1937.

WHITTERIDGE, GWENETH. *The Royal Hospital of St. Bartholomew.* 1951.

WILKS, SAMUEL and BETTANY, G. T. *Biographical History of Guy's Hospital.* 1892.

WILLIAMS, J. H. HARLEY. *A Century of Public Health in Britain 1832–1929.* Black, 1932.

WILLIS, J. C. *Florence Nightingale.* Unwin, 1931.

WILSON, W. J. E. *History of the Middlesex Hospital.*

WISE, A. R. J. *Your Hospital—Heritage and Future.* Heinemann, 1949.

WOODHAM-SMITH, CECIL. *Florence Nightingale.* Constable, 1950.

Parliamentary Papers

Report of Select Committee on Madhouses, 1763.

Report of Select Committee on the State of Criminal and Pauper Lunatics in England and Wales, 1807.

Report of Select Committee on Madhouses, 1815.

Report of Select Committee on Madhouses, 1816.

Report of Select Committee on Pauper Lunatics and Lunatics Acts, 1827.

Journals

The Hospital. Published monthly by the Institute of Hospital Administrators.

The British Medical Journal.

The Lancet.

INDEX

ACTON Society Trust, 170
Addenbrooke, John, 85
Addenbrooke's Hospital, Cambridge, 85
Alexander, Henry, 156
Alfune, 19
All Saints' Sisterhood, 114
Almoners, 126
Amputations, 40, 43, 44, 46, 87
Anaesthetics, 98, 122
Anatomy Act, 1832, 92
Anatomy (study of), 28, 53, 90
Anderson, Elizabeth Garrett, 96
Antiseptic surgery, 121
Apothecaries, 56, 57, 66, 70, 78, 80, 89, 108
Apprentices, medical, 42, 60, 77, 83, 84, 109, 110
Aseptic surgery, 122
Association for the Improvement of the Infirmaries of London Workhouses, 112
Athelstan, King, 17, 21
Atkinson Morley Hospital, Wimbledon, 96

BARBER-SURGEONS, 34, 38
Barking, 142
Barnes Hospital, Cheadle, 96
Bath General Hospital, 79
Battie, Dr. William, 147
Becket, Thomas, 19, 26
Beds, 28, 35, 36, 47, 49, 54, 76, 81, 88, 101
Belgrave Hospital for Children, London, 95
Bethel Hospital, Norwich, 145
Bethlem Hospital, London, 32, 33, 140, 141, 142–5, 154, 155, 157, 158, 163, 166
Black Death, 50
Boards of Governors, 168
Body-snatchers, 90–2
Bridewell Hospital, London, 33, 52, 142, 143
Bristol Royal Infirmary, 85–8, 91, 103, 105, 124
British Expeditionary Force, 137
British Medical Association, 136, 167
British Red Cross Society, 133, 174
Broadmoor, 164
Bromfield, William, 80
Brompton Hospital for Diseases of the Chest, 96, 106

Brownlow Hill Infirmary, Liverpool, 118
Bugs, 36, 47, 68, 71, 76, 81
Burke, William, 91
Burton Lazars, 33

CAMBRIDGE, 32, 34, 85, 142
Cancer, 28, 80
Canterbury, 12, 23, 26, 28
Cave, Viscount, 133
Central London Hospital for Throat, Nose and Ear, 95
Chaplains, 70, 74, 157
Charles I, 56
Charlesworth, Dr., 161
Children's hospitals, 95
Chloroform, 98, 122
Christ's Hospital, London, 33, 52, 142
City of London Maternity Hospital, 93
Clay, Rotha M., 18
Clerks, 67, 68, 70
Cockburn, Patrick, 62
Collectors, 30
Commissioners in Lunacy, 162–3
Committee of Enquiry into the Cost of the National Health Service, 169
Conolly, Dr., 162
Convalescent homes, 96
Cooper, Lady Diana, 130
Copland, Robert, 31
Cottage hospitals, 127–8
Cranleigh, 127
Cromwell, Thomas, 50
Crooke, Dr. Hilkiah, 143

DEVON and Exeter Hospital, 88
Dressers, 83, 109
D'Vebre, Mrs. D., 149

EAST London Hospital for Children, 95
Edward I, 29
Edward II, 23, 31
Edward VI, 33, 51
Elizabeth Garrett Anderson Hospital, London, 96
Emergency Medical Service, 136
Evelyn, John, 144
Exeter Eye Hospital, 94

FAIRS, 29
Fallowes, Dr., 148, 149
Fevers, 95, 171
Fistula, 28

Fliedner, Pastor, 114
Food, 28, 45, 46, 54, 75, 80, 81, 85, 88, 100, 101, 158
Free Cancer Hospital, Fulham, 94
French Protestant Hospital, London, 61
Fry, Elizabeth, 113
Fuel, 22, 28

GALE, Thomas, 38
General Lying-in Hospital, London, 93
Gloucester, 159
Gloucester Infirmary, 88
Godric, 26
Great Fire of London, 58
Great Ormond Street Children's Hospital, London, 94, 95, 126
Great Plague, 58
Gregory, William, 142
Grosvenor Hospital for Women, London, 95
Guy, Thomas, 68–9
Guy's Hospital, 60, 68–71, 83, 101, 106, 110, 119, 120, 124, 125, 130, 145, 172

HARBLEDOWN, 18, 23, 29, 30
Hare, William, 91
Harrison, John, 71
Haughton-le-Skerne, 26
Henry I, 19
Henry III, 22, 28
Henry IV, 140
Henry VI, 17
Henry VII, 141
Henry VIII, 32, 33, 34, 50, 53, 142
Herbert, Sidney, 115
Hereford General Infirmary, 88
Hill, Gardiner, 161
Hoare, Henry, 62, 63
Hospital for Diseases of the Throat, London, 95
Hospital for Sick Children, London, 94, 95, 126
Hospital Management Committees, 139, 168, 170, 171
Hospital Saturday Fund, 127
Hospital Sunday Fund, 127
Hospitallers, 42, 44
Hoxton, 157
Huguenots, 61
Hull Royal Infirmary, 88

INCHTUTHILL, 11, 17
Incurables, 96

JEPSON, George, 153
Jews, 25
John (King), 29
John of Gaddesdon, 12
Jones, Agnes, 118

KAISERSWERTH, 114
Kensington Children's Hospital, 94
Kent Dispensary, 88
King Edward VII Sanatorium, Midhurst, 173
King Edward's Hospital Fund for London, 127
King's College Hospital, London, 114
Kingston and Malden Victoria Medical Foundation, 173
Kingston Hospital, 173
Knightsbridge, 32

LACOCK, 11
Lanfranc, 18, 23
Layton, Richard, 50
Lazar houses, 18, 32
Leagues of Friends, 170, 174
Lechlade, 25
Leeds Infirmary, 88
Leicester Infirmary, 88
Lepers, 18, 20, 24, 25, 29, 32
Lettsom, John C., 93, 95
Lincoln Asylum, 159, 161
Lincoln County Hospital, 88
Lister, Lord, 121
Liston, Robert, 122
Liverpool Infirmary for Children, 94, 95
Liverpool Royal Infirmary, 88
Liverpool Royal Lunatic Asylum, 151
Local Government Act, 1929, 134
Lock hospitals, 32, 171
London, 18, 19, 23, 24, 32, 35–85, 141
London County Council, 134
London Fever Hospital, 94, 95
London Homoeopathic Hospital, 94
London Hospital, 71, 84, 91, 102, 105, 108, 120
London Lock Hospital, 79, 80, 93
London School of Medicine for Women, 96
London Skin Hospital, 95
London Smallpox Hospital, 94
London Voluntary Hospitals Committee, 134
Longspée, William, 29
Lunacy Act, 1890, 163
Lunatics Act, 1845, 163
Lying-in hospitals, 79, 80, 93

MADAN, Martin, 80
Manchester Hospital for Children, 94
Manchester Royal Infirmary, 88, 89, 98, 99, 102, 108, 109, 126
Manchester Royal Lunatic Asylum, 151, 152
Manningham, Sir Richard, 80
Manor House Hospital, London, 173
Margate, 93

Marsden, Dr. William, 103
Matrons, 21, 25, 41, 43, 52, 53, 63, 66, 70, 74, 78, 80, 107, 170
Medical Planning Commission, 136
Medical schools, 42, 76, 90
Mental hospitals, 140–66
Metropolitan Asylums Board, 112, 164
Metropolitan Commissioners in Lunacy, 160, 162
Metropolitan Convalescent Home, 96
Metropolitan Ear, Nose and Throat Hospital, 94
Metropolitan Poor Act, 1867, 112
Middlesex Asylum, 161, 162
Middlesex County Hospital, 79, 93
Middlesex Hospital, 78, 83, 84, 85, 105, 114, 115, 122, 166
Miller Hospital, London, 88
Ministry of Health, 136, 169
Mirfield, John, 36
Moorfields Eye Hospital, 94
More, Sir Thomas, 33

NAPPER, Albert, 127
National Dental Hospital, London, 95
National Health Service, 138, 139, 167–75
National Health Service Act, 1946, 139, 165, 167, 170
National Hospital for Diseases of the Heart, London, 94
National Hospital for Paralysis and Epilepsy, London, 94
National League of Hospital Friends, 170
New Hospital for Women, London, 96
New Victoria Hospital, New Malden, 173
Nightingale, Florence, 114–18
Nightingale School of Nursing, 115, 116
Norris (mental patient), 154
Norwich, 11, 95, 159
Nottingham General Hospital, 88, 102, 107, 108
Nuffield Provincial Hospitals Trust, 136, 167
Nurses, 42, 59, 70, 72, 74, 82, 105–7, 113, 114, 119, 120

ODIHAM, 35
Opie, Amelia, 113
Order of St. John, 133, 174
Ospringe, 23, 24
Out-patients, 46, 60, 76, 103, 123, 126
Oxford, 22, 23, 32

PARÉ, Ambroise, 15
Paris, Matthew, 23
Pest houses, 35
Physicians, 38, 39, 53, 56, 60, 70
Pilgrims, 17

Political and Economic Planning, 135
Pontefract, 27
Poor Law Amendment Act, 1834, 111
Poor Law infirmaries, 111, 112, 118, 129, 134, 135
Poplar Hospital for Accidents, 94
Porters, 67
Princess Margaret Hospital, Swindon, 172
Public Health Act, 1875, 112

QUEEN Charlotte's Lying-in Hospital, London, 80, 93
Queen's Hospital for Children, London, 95

RADCLIFFE Infirmary, Oxford, 88, 99–102, 104, 124
Rahere, 18, 19, 36
Rathbone, William, 118
Reed, Dr. Andrew, 96
Regional Hospital Boards, 139, 165, 167, 168
Retreat (The), York, 152–4, 165, 173
Romans, 11, 17
Röntgen, Wilhelm, 122
Royal British Pension Fund for Nurses, 120
Royal College of Physicians, 34
Royal Dental Hospital, London, 94
Royal Ear Hospital, London, 94
Royal Eye Hospital, London, 94
Royal Free Hospital, London, 104
Royal Hampshire County Hospital, Winchester, 61, 85
Royal Hospital for Diseases of the Chest, London, 94
Royal Hospital and Home for Incurables, Putney, 94, 96
Royal hospitals, 33, 35, 52
Royal Masonic Hospital, London, 173
Royal National Orthopaedic Hospital, London, 94
Royal Northern Hospital, London, 120, 123, 124, 126
Royal Sea-Bathing Hospital, Margate, 93
Royal Southern Hospital, Liverpool, 122, 124
Royal Waterloo Hospital for Children and Women, London, 94
Royal Westminster Ophthalmic Hospital, 94

ST. Albans, 17
St. Bartholomew's Hospital, Buckland, 20, 26
St. Bartholomew's Hospital, London, 18, 19, 23, 26, 32, 33, 35–48, 80, 90, 97, 98, 110, 119
St. Bartholomew's Hospital Home, Swanley, 96

St. Cross Hospital, Winchester, 24, 31
St. George's Hospital, Hyde Park Corner, 65–7, 85, 100, 104, 106, 107, 109, 122
St. James's Hospital, Chichester, 27
St. John's Hospital, Canterbury, 23
St. John's Hospital, Oxford, 22, 23, 28
St. John's Hospital, Stafford, 23
St. John's Hospital, Winchester, 30
St. John's House, 113
St. Leonard's Hospital, Derby, 31
St. Leonard's Hospital, Lancaster, 24
St. Leonard's Hospital, York, 21, 22, 23, 24, 30, 32
St. Luke's Hospital, London, 145–7, 159, 164–6
St. Mark's Hospital for Cancer, London, 94
St. Mary Abbot's Hospital, Kensington, 138
St. Mary Magdalene's Hospital, Southampton, 29
St. Mary Overie, Priory of, 19, 49
St. Mary's Hospital, Chichester, 14, 27
St. Mary's Hospital, London, 32, 33
St. Nicholas's Hospital, Pontefract, 27
St. Nicholas's Hospital, York, 26
St. Peter's Hospital, Bristol, 145
St. Peter's Hospital for Stone, London, 95
St. Peter's Hospital, York, 17, 21
St. Thomas's Hospital, Canterbury, 28
St. Thomas's Hospital, London, 19, 32, 33, 35, 39, 49–60, 68, 80, 83, 90, 101, 104, 106, 110, 115, 116, 117, 118, 125, 137, 172
St. Wulstan's Hospital, Worcester, 18
Samaritan Free Hospital for Women, London, 94
Sanitary Act, 1866, 112
Sankey Commission, 135, 167
Sankey, Viscount, 135
Savoy, Hospital, London, 24, 29
Saxons, 17
Scutari, 114, 115
Sea-Bathing Infirmary, Margate, 93, 95
Secretaries, 66, 72, 108, 170
Shaftesbury, Earl of, 160
Sherburn, 27, 28, 29
Shrewsbury Infirmary, 88
Simpson, Sir James, 98, 122
Sisters, 21, 25, 41, 44, 49, 55, 59, 70, 107
Smallpox, 48, 93, 171
Smithfield, 19
Southampton, 29
Southey, Robert, 113
Southwark, 32, 49, 54, 59
Southwark Cathedral, 19
South-West Metropolitan Regional Hospital Board, 173
Stafford, 23, 159

Stephen (King), 21
Stewards, 44, 107
Stewart, Dr. Alexander, 63–5
Stow, John, 141
Strand Workhouse, 111
Surgeons, 38, 39, 42, 52, 53, 56, 60, 70

TAUNTON and Somerset Hospital, Taunton, 96–7, 102
Taverner, Peter, 140–1
Teaching hospitals, 167–8
Temperance Hospital, London, 125
Treasurers, 42, 70
Tuberculosis, 93, 95, 96, 171
Tuke, William, 152

UNIFORM, 36, 43, 44, 119, 120
United Barber-Surgeons' Company, 34, 38, 43, 53, 90
University College, London, 111
University College Hospital, London, 111, 122

VENEREAL disease, 32, 57, 89, 93, 171
Vicary, Thomas, 38
Victoria Hospital, Kingston-on-Thames, 173
Victoria Park Hospital for Diseases of the Heart and Lungs, 94
Voluntary Hospitals Commission, 135

WAKEFIELD, 159
Wakefield Hospital, 88
Wardropper, Mrs., 115, 116, 117
Webb, Sidney and Beatrice, 112
West, Dr. Charles, 95
Westminster, 12, 13, 35, 62, 107
Westminster Hospital, 63–5, 67, 79, 82, 83, 98, 101, 103, 107, 114, 119, 124
Whitbread, Samuel, 80
Whittington, Richard, 50
Winchester, 24, 30, 31, 61
Witham, Robert, 62
Wogan, William, 62, 63
Women's Voluntary Service, 174
Woodall, John, 39
Worcester Royal Infirmary, 88, 89, 103, 104, 106, 107, 109, 124, 125
Workhouse infirmaries, 111, 112, 118, 129, 134–5
Wulstan, Bishop, 18

X-RAYS, 122

YORK, 17, 21, 23, 24, 26, 30, 102
York Asylum, 151, 156